MATHEMATICS

Statistics
Unit S2

COLEG GLAN HAFREN

Dr I G Evans

AS/A LEVEL

WJEC AS/A Level Mathematics
Statistics Unit S2

Published by the Welsh Joint Education Committee
245 Western Avenue, Cardiff, CF5 2YX

First published 2001

Printed by Hackman Printers Ltd
Clydach Vale, Tonypandy, Rhondda, CF40 2XX

ISBN: 1 86085 461 3

PREFACE

This book covers the specification for Unit S2 of the new WJEC scheme for A/AS Mathematics. As in the book covering the specification for Unit S1, every chapter has been sectionalised, each section introducing a specific topic followed by worked examples and exercises. At the end of each chapter there is a selection of A Level questions on the topics covered in the chapter. Numerical answers to all the exercises are given at the end of the book, together with an index of the topics covered.

Chapter 1 covers continuous distribution and is virtually identical to that in the Module S1 book but with the additional section (§ 1.2) on the percentiles of a continuous distribution.

Chapter 2 deals with two or more random variables (discrete and continuous) and again is virtually identical to the coverage in the Module S1 book.

Chapter 3 covers some of the topics on hypotheses testing included in the Module S2 book.

As in the Unit S1 book, the tables used in the worked examples are *Elementary Statistical Tables* published originally by RND (Cardiff) but are now being published by the WJEC.

Notification of any errors that may be found in this book would be appreciated and should be sent to the author or to the WJEC.

CONTENTS

Chapter 1

Continuous Random Variables

Introduction

In Section 4.1 of Book S1 a random variable was defined as being a verbal description of a rule for assigning a numerical value to every outcome of a random experiment. Every random variable studied in Chapter 4 of Book S1 was such that its possible values could be listed individually, defined to be a discrete random variable. The possible values of such a random variable and their probabilities of occurring was referred to as the probability distribution of the random variable.

In this chapter we shall be considering random variables that are not discrete, that is, random variables whose possible values cannot be listed individually. As in Chapter 4 of Book S1, such a random variable will be denoted by a capital letter (e.g. V, W, X, Y, Z).

Definition

A random variable whose possible values cannot be listed individually is defined to be a **continuous** random variable.

Here, we shall restrict consideration to continuous random variables whose possible values are expressed as intervals. Some examples of such continuous random variables are as follows.

(1)   V = The arrival time of a particular train at a railway station,

(2)   W = The height of a pupil chosen at random.

(3)   X = The operational lifetime of an electric light bulb.

(4)   Y = The distance a shot is from the centre of a target.

(5)   Z = The maximum temperature in Cardiff tomorrow.

Since the possible values of a continuous random variable cannot be listed individually a method different from that in Chapter 4 of Book S1 is necessary to describe how the one unit of probability is distributed over its possible values.

1.1 Probability density function

Suppose X is a continuous random variable with possible values $a \leq x \leq b$. The one unit of probability has to be distributed over the interval [a, b]. This may be done in infinitely many ways. Imagine the one unit of probability as being powder in a jug and is poured over the interval [a, b]. The following diagrams show some possibilities. In each case the enclosed area is equal to unity (the total probability).

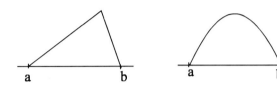

For a mathematical description of the probability distribution of a continuous random variable, let f(x) denote the height of the 'mound' of probability above the value x, as indicated in Figure 1. Since the total area of the 'mound' is unity it follows that

$$\int_a^b f(x)\,dx \quad = \quad 1 \tag{1}$$

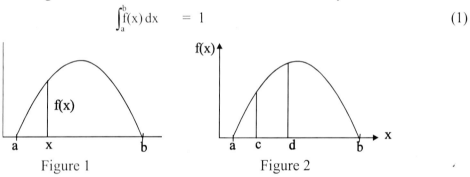

Figure 1　　　　　　　　Figure 2

Furthermore, as illustrated in Figure 2, the amount of probability allocated to the subinterval [c, d] is the area under f(x) above [c, d]. It follows that the probability of the event $(c \leq X \leq d)$ occurring is given by

$$P(c \leq X \leq d) \quad = \quad \int_c^d f(x)\,dx \,. \tag{2}$$

Definition. Any function f such that

$$f(x) \geq 0, \quad \text{for} \quad a \leq x \leq b,$$

and
$$\int_a^b f(x)\,dx \quad = \quad 1$$

is referred to as a **probability density function**.

Such a function is appropriate for describing the probability distribution of a continuous random variable X having possible values $a \leq x \leq b$.

Note that it is an area under the curve f(x) which represents a probability. For any possible value x of X, f(x) is a measure of the **density** of concentration of probability in the vicinity of x. For any value c in [a, b], we have $P(X = c) = 0$, since the area under f(x) above the point $x = c$ is zero, the line $x = c$ having no thickness. In particular, note that

$$P(c \leq X \leq d) \; = \; P(c < X \leq d) \; = \; P(c \leq X < d) \; = \; P(c < X < d).$$

Thus, when considering a probability such as $P(c \leq X \leq d)$ when X is continuous we may replace either or both symbols $\leq$ by $<$, which is not true when X is discrete.

Example 1

The continuous random variable X is distributed with probability density function f given by $\qquad\qquad f(x) \; = \; kx(4 - x), \quad$ for $\; 0 \leq x \leq 4.$

Find (a) the value of k, (b) $P(X \leq 3)$, (c) $P(0 < X < 1 \mid X \leq 3)$.

[It has become customary to define f(x) for all x so that in the above example there would be an added line stating "f(x) = 0, otherwise". However, for consistency with what we did for a discrete random variable we shall not be following this custom, it being understood that $f(x) = 0$ for all values of x other than those specified.]

Solution

(a) We find k by using (1) above; that is

$$k \int_0^4 (4x - x^2)\,dx \quad = \; 1.$$

On integrating we get

$$k\left[2x^2 - \frac{1}{3}x^3 \right]_0^4 \quad = \; 1,$$

leading to $\qquad\qquad k\left[32 - \frac{64}{3} \right] \quad = \; 1 \;$ and $\; k \; = \; \frac{3}{32}.$

(b) Using (2) above we have

$$P(X \leq 3) \; = \; \frac{3}{32} \int_0^3 (4x - x^2)\,dx \; = \; \frac{3}{32}\left[2x^2 - \frac{1}{3}x^3 \right]_0^3 \; = \; \frac{27}{32}.$$

(c) From the definition of conditional probability

$$P(0 < X < 1 \mid X \leq 3) \; = \; \frac{P(0 < X < 1 \cap X \leq 3)}{P(X \leq 3)} \; = \; \frac{P(0 < X < 1)}{P(X \leq 3)}.$$

$$P(0 < X < 1) \; = \; \frac{3}{32}\left[2x^2 - \frac{1}{3}x^3 \right]_0^1 \; = \; \frac{5}{32}.$$

Hence, $\qquad P(0 < X < 1 \mid X \leq 3) \; = \; \frac{5}{32} \div \frac{27}{32} \; = \; \frac{5}{27}.$

Example 2

The continuous random variable X has probability density function f given by

$$f(x) = \frac{1}{2x^2}, \qquad \text{for } 1 \le x \le 3,$$

$$f(x) = \frac{1}{18}, \qquad \text{for } 3 < x \le 15.$$

Evaluate (a) $P(2 < X < 3)$, (b) $P(X > 10)$, (c) $P(2 < X < 6)$, (d) $P(X < 6)$.

Solution

(a) Since $f(x) = \dfrac{1}{2x^2}$ for all x from 2 to 3,

$$P(2 < X < 3) = \int_2^3 \frac{1}{2x^2} dx = \left[-\frac{1}{2x} \right]_2^3 = \frac{1}{4} - \frac{1}{6} = \frac{1}{12}.$$

(b) Since $f(x) = \dfrac{1}{18}$ for all x from 10 to 15

$$P(X > 10) = \frac{1}{18} \int_{10}^{15} dx = \frac{1}{18} \left[x \right]_{10}^{15} = \frac{5}{18}.$$

(c) Since $f(x)$ takes different forms for $1 \le x \le 3$ and for $3 < x \le 15$ we shall use

$$(2 < X < 6) = (2 < X \le 3) \cup (3 < X < 6),$$

so that $P(2 < X < 6) = P(2 < X \le 3) + P(3 < X < 6)$

$$= \int_2^3 \frac{1}{2x^2} dx + \int_3^6 \frac{1}{18} dx$$

$$= \left[-\frac{1}{2x} \right]_2^3 + \frac{1}{18} \left[x \right]_3^6 = \frac{1}{12} + \frac{1}{6} = \frac{1}{4}.$$

(d) To evaluate $P(X < 6)$ we could proceed as in (c) above but it is easier to find the probability of the complementary event $(X \ge 6)$.

$$P(X < 6) = 1 - P(X \ge 6) = 1 - \int_6^{15} \frac{1}{18} dx = 1 - \frac{1}{18} \left[x \right]_6^{15} = \frac{1}{2}.$$

Exercise 1.1

1. The random variable X has the probability density function f where

    $$f(x) = cx(16 - x^2), \text{ for } 0 \le x \le 4.$$

    Evaluate (a) c, (b) $P(1 < X < 2)$, (c) $P(X \ge 3)$, (d) $P(X > 2 \mid 1 < X < 3)$

2. The operational lifetimes in hours of certain batteries are distributed with probability density function f, where

    $$f(x) = \frac{c}{x^2}, \text{ for } 100 \le x \le 400.$$

Find the value of c and the probability that the operational lifetime of such a battery will lie between 150 and 200 hours.

3. The random variable X is distributed with probability density function f, where
$$f(x) = k(1 - x^4), \quad \text{for} -1 \le x \le 1.$$
Evaluate (a) $P\left(X > \dfrac{1}{2}\right)$, (b) $P\left(X^2 > \dfrac{1}{4}\right)$, (c) $P\left(X < \dfrac{1}{2} \Big| X > 0\right)$.

4. The duration, X minutes, of a telephone call by a certain person to a friend is a continuous random variable X having probability density function f given by
$$f(x) = x^{-2}, \quad \text{for } x \ge 1,$$

(a) Calculate the probability that the duration of such a call will be (i) between 5 and 10 minutes, (ii) less than 5 minutes.

(b) Given that a call has already lasted 3 minutes, calculate the conditional probability that the duration of the call will be less than 5 minutes.

5. A person fires a rifle at a circular target of radius 4 cm on which are drawn circles of radii 1 cm, 2 cm, and 3 cm, all centred at the centre of the target. The distance X cm of the point of impact of a shot from the centre of the target is distributed with probability density function f, where
$$f(x) = 0.03(x^2 + 3), \quad \text{for } 0 \le x \le 4.$$

(a) Find the probability that a shot will hit the target inside the innermost circle.

(b) A shot inside the innermost circle scores 4 points; a shot between the innermost and middle circles scores 2 points; a shot between the middle and outermost circles scores 1 point; and a shot outside the outermost circle scores nothing. Calculate (i) the most probable score from a single shot, (ii) the mean score per shot.

6. The random variable X is distributed with probability density function f, where
$$f(x) = \frac{3}{7}x^2, \quad \text{for } 0 \le x \le 1,$$
$$f(x) = \frac{3}{7}, \quad \text{for } 1 < x \le 3.$$
Evaluate (a) $P\left(X > 1\dfrac{1}{2}\right)$, (b) $P\left(X < \dfrac{1}{2}\right)$, (c) $P\left(X < 2\dfrac{1}{2}\right)$, (d) $P\left(\dfrac{1}{2} < X < 2\right)$.

7. The continuous random variable X has probability density function f, where
$$f(x) = \frac{1}{2}x, \quad \text{for } 0 < x < 1,$$
$$f(x) = \frac{1}{6}(4 - x), \quad \text{for } 1 \le x \le 4.$$
Evaluate (a) $P(X < 2)$, (b) $P(X < \frac{1}{2} \mid X < 2)$

8. The continuous random variable X has probability density function f, where

$$f(x) = \frac{x}{4}, \quad \text{for } 0 \leq x \leq 2,$$

$$f(x) = \frac{4}{x^3}, \quad \text{for } x > 2.$$

(a) Evaluate (i) P(X < 3), (ii) P(1 < X < 3).

(b) Find the value of k if P(X < k) = 0.995.

9. A garage is supplied with petrol every Monday morning and its weekly demand in thousands of litres is a random variable X whose probability density function is f, where

$$f(x) = \frac{3}{125}(5 - x)^2, \quad \text{for } 0 < x < 5.$$

Find (a) the probability that the garage's sales in a week will be less than 3000 litres, (b) the probability that the garage will not be able to meet the demand in a week, given that the capacity of its supply tank is 4000 litres.

10. The continuous random variable X has probability density function f, where

$$f(x) = \frac{a + x}{a^2}, \quad \text{for } -a \leq x < 0,$$

$$f(x) = \frac{a - x}{a^2}, \quad \text{for } 0 \leq x \leq a.$$

Evaluate (a) $P\left(X < \frac{1}{2}a\right)$, (b) $P\left(X^2 > \frac{1}{4}a^2\right)$.

1.2 Cumulative distribution function.

A probability distribution can also be described by means of the cumulative distribution function defined as follows.

Definition

For any random variable X, the function F such that

$$F(x) = P(X \leq x) \text{ for all } x,$$

is called the **cumulative distribution function** of X.

F(x) is the amount of probability that has been assigned up to the value x. Although defined for both discrete and continuous variables the cumulative distribution function is most useful for a continuous random variable.

Consider a continuous random variable with possible values a ≤ x ≤ b, and probability density function f. Its cumulative distribution function is F, where

$$F(x) = 0, \quad \text{for } x < a$$

$$F(x) = \int_a^x f(t)\, dt, \quad \text{for all } a \leq x \leq b, \tag{1}$$

$$F(x) = 1, \quad \text{for } x > b.$$

[The dummy variable t has been used in (1) so as to avoid having x in the integrand and as a limit].

It follows that

$$F(a) = 0 \quad \text{and} \quad F(b) = 1,$$

which provide useful checks on a derived cumulative distribution function, and for any constants c, d with c < d,

$$P(c \le X \le d) = P(c \le X < d) = P(c < X \le d) = P(c < X < d) = F(d) - F(c)$$

Example 1

Determine the cumulative distribution function of the random variable X whose probability density function f is given by

$$f(x) = kx(4 - x), \quad \text{for } 0 \le x \le 4.$$

[This was the distribution considered in Example 1 of Section 1.1.]

Solution

Let F denote the cumulative distribution function of X. We immediately have

$$F(x) = 0 \text{ for } x < 0 \text{ and } F(x) = 1 \text{ for } x > 4.$$

From (1), for $0 \le x \le 4$,

$$F(x) = \int_0^x kt(4 - t)\, dt = k\left[2t^2 - \frac{1}{3}t^3 \right]_0^x$$

$$= k\left(2x^2 - \frac{1}{3}x^3 \right).$$

Since F(4) must equal 1 we have

$$k\left(32 - \frac{64}{3} \right) = 1, \quad \text{so that} \quad k = \frac{3}{32}$$

(exactly as obtained in Example 1 of Section 1.1). Hence, the full specification for F is :

$$F(x) = 0, \quad \text{for } x < 0,$$

$$F(x) = \frac{3}{32}\left(2x^2 - \frac{1}{3}x^3 \right), \quad \text{for } 0 \le x \le 4$$

$$F(x) = 1, \quad \text{for } x > 4.$$

The graph of F(x) is as follows :

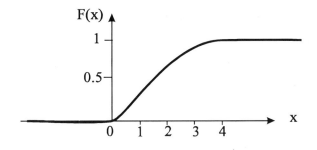

We can now use $F(x)$ to find the probabilities asked for in Example 1 of Section 1.1 as follows.

$$P(X \le 3) = F(3) = \frac{3}{32}\left(2 \times 9 - \frac{1}{3} \times 27\right) = \frac{27}{32}, \text{ as before.}$$

$$P(0 < X < 1) = P(X < 1) - P(X \le 0) = F(1) - F(0)$$
$$= \frac{3}{32}\left(2 - \frac{1}{3}\right) = \frac{5}{32}, \text{ as obtained earlier.}$$

Generalising the above, note that for any random variable X,
$$P(X > c) = 1 - P(X \le c) = 1 - F(c),$$
$$P(X \ge c) = 1 - P(X < c) = 1 - P(X \le c) = 1 - F(c),$$
$$P(c < X < d) = P(X < d) - P(X \le c) = F(d) - F(c).$$

Example 2

Find the cumulative distribution function of the random variable X whose probability density function f is given by

$$f(x) = \frac{1}{2x^2}, \qquad \text{for } 1 \le x \le 3,$$

$$f(x) = \frac{1}{18}, \qquad \text{for } 3 < x \le 15$$

(as in Example 2 of Section 1.1).

Solution

We immediately have $F(x) = 0$ for $x < 1$ and $F(x) = 1$ for $x > 15$.

For $1 \le x \le 15$, we have

$$F(x) = \int_1^x f(t)\,dt\,.$$

We now have to take account of the fact that f(t) has a different form for $t \le 3$ and for $t > 3$.

Consider a value of x in the range $1 \le x \le 3$. For such an x,

$$F(x) = \int_1^x \frac{1}{2t^2}\,dt = \left[-\frac{1}{2t}\right]_1^x = \frac{1}{2} - \frac{1}{2x}.$$

[As a check we note that $F(1) = 0$ as it should be.]

Now consider a value of x in the range $3 < x \le 15$. Recalling that $F(x) = P(X \le x)$ we have

$$F(x) = F(3) + \int_3^x \frac{1}{18}\,dt = \left(\frac{1}{2} - \frac{1}{6}\right) + \left[\frac{1}{18}t\right]_3^x$$

$$= \frac{1}{3} + \frac{1}{18}(x - 3) = \frac{1}{18}(x + 3).$$

[As a check we note that $F(15) = 1$ as it should be.]

Hence, the complete specification of F(x) is as follows :

$$F(x) = 0, \quad \text{for } x < 1,$$

$$F(x) = \frac{1}{2}\left(1 - \frac{1}{x}\right), \quad \text{for } 1 \le x \le 3$$

$$F(x) = \frac{1}{18}(x + 3), \quad \text{for } 3 < x \le 15$$

$$F(x) = 1, \quad \text{for } x > 15.$$

[Check: $F(1) = \frac{1}{2}\left(1 - \frac{1}{1}\right) = 0$ and $F(15) = \frac{1}{18}(15 + 3) = 1$, as required.]

Let us now use the above F(x) to evaluate the probabilities in Example 2 of Section 1.1.

(a) $\quad P(2 < X < 3) = F(3) - F(2) = \frac{1}{2}\left(1 - \frac{1}{3}\right) - \frac{1}{2}\left(1 - \frac{1}{2}\right) = \frac{1}{12}$.

(b) $\quad P(X > 10) = 1 - F(10) = 1 - \frac{1}{18}(10 + 3) = \frac{5}{18}$.

(c) $\quad P(X < 6) = F(6) = \frac{1}{18}(6 + 3) = \frac{1}{2}$.

All the answers agree with those obtained in Section 1.1.

Some properties of F(x)

F(x) was obtained by integrating f(x); reversing the operation it follows that f(x) is the derivative of F(x). That is

$$f(x) = \frac{dF(x)}{dx} \quad \text{for all possible values of x.} \tag{2}$$

Another useful property of F(x), when X is a continuous random variable, follows from the fact that $P(X < x) = P(X \le x)$. This is particularly relevant when the probability density function of X has a split form. For instance, suppose that f(x) has one form for $a \le x \le b$ and another form for $b < x \le c$, so that F(x) will also have different forms for these two ranges of x. However, it follows that each form of F(x) must give the same value for F(b) since $P(X \le b) = P(X < b)$. Mathematically, F is a continuous function.

Example 3

The continuous random variable X has cumulative distribution function F defined by

$$F(x) = 0, \quad \text{for } x < 0$$

$$F(x) = \frac{1}{3}x, \quad \text{for } 0 \le x \le 1,$$

$$F(x) = a, \qquad \text{for } 1 < x \le 2,$$
$$F(x) = bx^2, \qquad \text{for } 2 < x \le 3,$$
$$F(x) = \frac{x}{4}, \qquad \text{for } 3 < x \le 4,$$
$$F(x) = 1, \qquad \text{for } x > 4.$$

(a) Find the values of the constants a and b.

(b) Evaluate $P\left(\frac{1}{2} \le X \le 2\frac{1}{2}\right)$.

(c) Determine the probability density function of X.

Solution

(a) Using $F(x) = \frac{x}{3}$ for $0 \le x \le 1$ we find that $F(1) = \frac{1}{3}$. Using $F(x) = a$ for $1 < x \le 2$ we find that $F(1) = a$. Hence $a = \frac{1}{3}$.

Using $F(x) = a$ for $1 < x \le 2$ we find that $F(2) = a = \frac{1}{3}$. Using $F(x) = bx^2$ for $2 < x \le 3$ we find that $F(2) = 4b$. Hence $4b = \frac{1}{3}$, so that $b = \frac{1}{12}$.

(b) $P\left(\frac{1}{2} \le X \le 2\frac{1}{2}\right) = F\left(2\frac{1}{2}\right) - F\left(\frac{1}{2}\right) = \frac{1}{12}\left(2\frac{1}{2}\right)^2 - \frac{1}{3}\left(\frac{1}{2}\right) = \frac{17}{48}.$

(c) By differentiation, the probability density function f of X is given by

$$f(x) = 0, \qquad \text{for } x < 0$$
$$f(x) = \frac{1}{3}, \qquad \text{for } 0 \le x \le 1,$$
$$f(x) = 0, \qquad \text{for } 1 < x \le 2,$$
$$f(x) = 2bx = \frac{x}{6}, \qquad \text{for } 2 < x \le 3,$$
$$f(x) = \frac{1}{4}, \qquad \text{for } 3 < x \le 4,$$
$$f(x) = 0, \qquad \text{for } x > 4.$$

[Observe that unlike F(x), f(x) is not continuous everywhere since it has 'jumps' (discontinuities) at the values x = 0, 1, 2, 3 and 4.]

Exercise 1.2

1. The random variable X has cumulative distribution function F, where
$$F(x) = 0, \qquad \text{for } x < 3$$
$$F(x) = 1 - \frac{k}{x^2}, \qquad \text{for } x \ge 3.$$

(a) Find the value of k.

(b) Determine the probability density function of X.

2. The continuous random variable X has cumulative distribution function F, where

$$F(x) = 0, \qquad \text{for } x < 0,$$

$$F(x) = \frac{x^2}{10}, \qquad \text{for } 0 \le x < 2,$$

$$F(x) = 1 - k(5 - x)^2, \qquad \text{for } 2 \le x < 5,$$

$$F(x) = 1, \qquad \text{for } x \ge 5.$$

(a) Find the value of the constant k.

(b) Evaluate $P(1 \le X < 3)$ and $P(1 \le X < 4 \mid X < 3)$.

(c) Find the probability density function of X.

3. The continuous random variable X has cumulative distribution function F where

$F(x) = 0$ for $x < 0$, $F(x) = 1$ for $x > 3$,

$$F(x) = \frac{1}{2}x - \frac{1}{8}x^2, \qquad \text{for } 0 \le x \le 1,$$

$$F(x) = \frac{1}{4}x + a, \qquad \text{for } 1 < x \le 2,$$

$$F(x) = \frac{1}{8}x^2 - \frac{1}{4}x + b, \qquad \text{for } 2 < x \le 3.$$

(a) Find the values of a and b.

(b) Determine the probability density function of X.

4. The random variable X has cumulative distribution function F given by

$F(x) = 0$ for $x < -2$, $F(x) = 1$ for $x \ge 6$,

$$F(x) = \frac{x+2}{12}, \qquad \text{for } -2 < x < 0,$$

$$F(x) = a(x + 1), \qquad \text{for } 0 \le x < 4,$$

$$F(x) = b(x + 6), \qquad \text{for } 4 \le x < 6.$$

(a) Find the values of a and b.

(b) Determine the probability density function of X.

5. The continuous random variable X has possible values $0 < x \le 3$ and is such that

$$P(X > x) = a + bx^3 \qquad \text{for } 0 < x \le 3.$$

(a) Write down the cumulative distribution function of X.

(b) Find the values of a and b.

(c) Determine the probability density function of X.

1.3 Percentiles of a continuous distribution

Let X denote a continuous random variable having probability density function f and cumulative distribution function F.

Definition: For any p between 0 and 1 the value x_p such that

$$P(X \leq x_p) \equiv F(x_p) = p$$

is called the **100th percentile** of the distribution of X. Thus, the probability is p that a randomly observed value of X will be less than or equal to x_p. This is illustrated in the diagrams below.

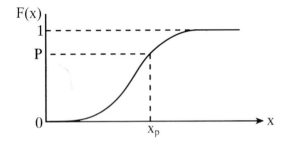 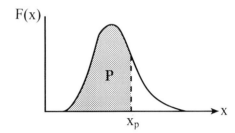

The most widely used percentiles are as follows:

$x_{0.5}$, which is called the **median** of the distribution,

$x_{0.25}$, which is called the **lower quartile** of the distribution,

$x_{0.75}$, which is called the **upper quartile** of the distribution.

The median is often used as a measure of location as an alternative to the mean (defined in Section 1.4) particularly when the distribution is skew. With the median as the measure of location an appropriate measure of spread is the difference between x_p and x_{1-p} for an appropriate choice of p. The most widely used ones are

(1) $x_{0.75}$ - $x_{0.25}$, which is known as the **interquartile range,**

$x_{0.25}$ being the **lower quartile** and $x_{0.75}$ the **upper quartile** of the distribution,

(2) $x_{0.9} - x_{0.1}$, which is known as the **10-90 interpercentile range,**

$x_{0.1}$ being the 10% percentile and $x_{0.9}$ the 90% percentile of the distribution.

Example 1

The continuous random variable X has probability density function f, where

$$f(x) = \frac{4}{3x^2} , \quad \text{for } 1 \leq x \leq 4.$$

Find an expression for x_p, the 100pth percentile of the distribution. Hence find, correct to two decimal places, the values of the median, the quartiles and the 80th percentile.

Solution

The cumulative distribution function F of X may be shown to be such that

$$F(x) = \frac{4}{3}\left(1 - \frac{1}{x}\right) , \quad \text{for } 1 \le x \le 4$$

The $100p^{th}$ percentile x_p is the solution of $F(x_p) = p$, that is of

$$\frac{4}{3}\left(1 - \frac{1}{x_p}\right) = p ,$$

from which we find that

$$x_p = \frac{1}{1 - 0 \cdot 75p} .$$

Setting $p = 0 \cdot 5, 0 \cdot 25, 0 \cdot 75$ and $0 \cdot 8$, respectively we have

the median $x_{0 \cdot 5} = 1/(1 - 0 \cdot 375) = 1 \cdot 6$

the lower quartile $x_{0 \cdot 25} = 1/(1 - 0 \cdot 1875) = 1 \cdot 23$ correct to two decimal places

the upper quartile $x_{0 \cdot 75} = 1/(1 - 0 \cdot 5625) = 2 \cdot 29$ correct to two decimal places

the 80th percentile $x_{0 \cdot 8} = 1/(1 - 0 \cdot 6) = 2 \cdot 5$.

Example 2

Find the median, the lower quartile and the 10-90 interpercentile range of the random variable X whose probability density function f is given by

$$f(x) = \frac{1}{2x^2} , \quad \text{for } 1 \le x \le 3,$$

$$f(x) = \frac{1}{18} , \quad \text{for } 3 < x \le 15 .$$

Solution

We showed in Example 2 of Section 1.2 that the cumulative distribution function F of X is such that

$$F(x) = \frac{1}{2}\left(1 - \frac{1}{x}\right) , \quad \text{for } 1 \le x \le 3,$$

$$F(x) = \frac{1}{18}(x + 3) , \quad \text{for } 3 < x \le 15.$$

On noting that $F(3) = \frac{1}{3}$, the value of x_p for any $p \le \frac{1}{3}$ will be in the interval $[1,3]$ and for any $p > \frac{1}{3}$ will be in the interval $(3,15]$. Since $0 \cdot 5$ is $> \frac{1}{3}$, the median is in the interval $(3,15]$ and is the solution of

$$\frac{1}{18}(x_{0 \cdot 5} + 3) = 0 \cdot 5 ,$$

the solution of which is $x_{0 \cdot 5} = 6$.

Since 0.25 is $< \frac{1}{3}$, the lower quartile $x_{0.25}$ is in the interval $(3,15]$ and is the solution of

$$\frac{1}{2}\left(1 - \frac{1}{x_{0.25}}\right) = 0.25.$$

On solving, the lower quartile is $x_{0.25} = 2$.

For the 10-90 interpercentile range we require the values of $x_{0.9}$ and $x_{0.1}$. Since 0.9 is $> \frac{1}{3}$, the 90th percentile is the solution of

$$\frac{1}{18}\left(x_{0.9} + 3\right) = 0.9,$$

which, on solving, gives $x_{0.9} = 13.2$. Since 0.1 is $< \frac{1}{3}$, the 10% percentile $x_{0.1}$ is the solution of

$$\frac{1}{2}\left(1 - \frac{1}{x_{0.1}}\right) = 0.1,$$

from which we find $x_{0.1} = 1.25$.

Thus, the 10-90 interpercentile range is $13.2 - 1.25 = 11.95$.

Exercise 1.3

1. For each of the following distributions find an expression for the $100p^{th}$ percentile and hence evaluate the median and the quartiles of the distribution, giving your answers correct to two decimal places when appropriate.

(a) $f(x) = \dfrac{1}{x^2}$, for $x > 1$.

(b) $f(x) = 0.2$, for $1 \le x \le 6$.

(c) $f(x) = kx^2$, for $1 \le x \le 2$.

(d) $f(x) = \dfrac{4}{(x + 2)^2}$, for $0 \le x \le 2$.

2. Find, correct to three decimal places, the median, the quartiles and the 10-90 interpercentile range of each of the following distributions.

(a) $\quad f(x) = \dfrac{1}{5}$, for $0 \le x \le 1$,

$\quad\quad f(x) = \dfrac{x^3}{25}$, for $1 < x \le 3$.

(b) $\quad f(x) = \dfrac{2}{3}$, for $0 \le x < 1$,

$\quad\quad f(x) = \dfrac{1}{3}$, for $1 \le x \le 2$.

(c) $\quad f(x) = 0.1x - 0.3$, for $4 \le x \le 6$

$\quad\quad f(x) = 0.3$ $\quad\quad\quad\quad$ for $6 < x \le 8$.

3. The continuous random variable X has probability density function f given by

$$f(x) = \frac{x}{2}, \quad \text{for } 0 \le x \le 1,$$

$$f(x) = \frac{(4-x)}{6}, \quad \text{for } 1 < x \le 4.$$

(a) Show that the cumulative distribution function F of X is such that

$$F(x) = 1 - \frac{1}{12}(4-x)^2, \quad \text{for } 1 < x \le 4,$$

and find an expression for F(x) valid for $0 \le x \le 1$.

(b) Hence determine the median, the quartiles, and the 20-80 interpercentile range of the distribution, giving your answers correct to two decimal places.

4. The continuous random variable X has probability density function f given by

$$f(x) = ax - bx^2, \quad \text{for } 0 \le x \le 2.$$

Given that the median value of X is equal to 1, determine the values of a and b.

1.4 Mean and variance of a continuous random variable

Let h(X) be a function of the continuous random variable X having possible values $a \le x \le b$ and probability density function f. As an extension to the definition given in Section 2.3 of Book S1 when X is discrete, the **expected value** of h(X) is defined to be

$$E[h(X)] = \int_a^b h(x)f(x)\,dx. \tag{1}$$

In particular, E(X) is the **mean**, μ, of the distribution of X, and $E[(X - \mu)^2]$ is the **variance** of the distribution of X. As shown in Book S1

$$\text{Var}(X) = E[(X - \mu)^2] = E(X^2) - \mu^2. \tag{2}$$

The properties of E derived in Chapter 4 of Book 1 are also valid when X is continuous and may be verified on using properties of definite integrals. In particular, for any constants c_1, c_2 and any functions $h_1(X)$, $h_2(X)$,

$$E[c_1 h_1(X) + c_2 h_2(X)] = c_1 E[h_1(X)] + c_2 E[h_2(X)]. \tag{3}$$

This result extends in an obvious way to a linear combination of three or more functions of X.

It follows from (3) that

$$E(aX + b) = aE(X) + b, \tag{4}$$

and, following the derivation given in Section 4.4 of Book S1, that

$$\text{Var}(aX + b) = a^2 \text{Var}(X). \tag{5}$$

These two results enable us to find the mean and the variance of Y = aX + b without first having to find the distribution of Y.

Furthermore, the mean and the variance of Z = h(X), for any function h(X), can also be found without knowing its distribution. The mean of Z can be calculated using (1). Now,

$$\text{Var}(Z) = E(Z^2) - [E(Z)]^2 = E[h^2(X)] - \{E[h(X)]\}^2$$

and both quantities on the right-hand side can be calculated using (1).

The above results are illustrated in the examples that follow.

Example 1

The continuous random variable X is distributed with probability density function f, where

$$f(x) = 6x(1-x), \qquad \text{for } 0 \le x \le 1.$$

(a) Find the mean and the variance of X.

(b) Deduce the mean and variance of (i) Y = 10X − 3, (ii) Z = 2(3 − X)/5.

(c) Evaluate $E(5X^2 - 3X + 1)$.

(d) Find the mean and variance of $W = X^{1/2}$.

Solution

(a) The mean of X is

$$E(X) = \int_0^1 6x^2(1-x)\,dx = 6\int_0^1 (x^2 - x^3)\,dx$$

$$= 6\left[\frac{1}{3}x^3 - \frac{1}{4}x^4\right]_0^1 = 6\left(\frac{1}{3} - \frac{1}{4}\right) = \frac{1}{2}.$$

$$E(X^2) = 6\int_0^1 x^3(1-x)\,dx = 6\int_0^1 (x^3 - x^4)\,dx$$

$$= 6\left[\frac{1}{4}x^4 - \frac{1}{5}x^5\right]_0^1 = 6\left(\frac{1}{4} - \frac{1}{5}\right) = \frac{6}{20}.$$

Therefore, $\quad \text{Var}(X) = \dfrac{6}{20} - \left(\dfrac{1}{2}\right)^2 = \dfrac{1}{20}.$

(b) The mean and the variance of Y and Z can be deduced using (4) and (5).

(i) The mean of Y is $\quad E(10X - 3) = 10E(X) - 3 = 10 \times \dfrac{1}{2} - 3 = 2.$

The variance of Y is $\quad \text{Var}(10X - 3) = 10^2\text{Var}(X) = 100 \times \dfrac{1}{20} = 5.$

(ii) The mean of Z is $\quad E\left[\dfrac{2}{5}(3-X)\right] = E\left(\dfrac{6}{5} - \dfrac{2}{5}X\right) = \dfrac{6}{5} - \dfrac{2}{5} \times \dfrac{1}{2} = 1.$

The variance of Z is $\quad \text{Var}\left(\dfrac{6}{5} - \dfrac{2}{5}X\right) = \dfrac{4}{25}\text{Var}(X) = \dfrac{1}{125}.$

(c) Using (3), $\quad E(5X^2 - 3X + 1) = 5E(X^2) - 3E(X) + 1 = 5 \times \dfrac{6}{20} - 3 \times \dfrac{1}{2} + 1 = 1.$

(d) From (1),

$$E(W) = E(X^{1/2}) = 6\int_0^1 x^{1/2} \times x(1-x)\,dx = 6\int_0^1 (x^{3/2} - x^{5/2})\,dx$$

$$= 6\left[\dfrac{2}{5}x^{5/2} - \dfrac{2}{7}x^{7/2}\right]_0^1 = 6\left(\dfrac{2}{5} - \dfrac{2}{7}\right) = 6 \times \dfrac{4}{35} = \dfrac{24}{35}.$$

$$E(W^2) = E(X) = \dfrac{1}{2}, \text{ as shown in (a).}$$

Hence, $\quad Var(W) = E(W^2) - [E(W)]^2 = \dfrac{1}{2} - \left(\dfrac{24}{35}\right)^2 = \dfrac{73}{2450}.$

Example 2

Find the mean and the variance of the distribution having probability density function f given by

$$f(x) = x, \qquad \text{for } 0 \le x \le 1,$$
$$f(x) = 2 - x, \qquad \text{for } 1 < x \le 2.$$

Solution

The mean is $\quad E(X) = \displaystyle\int_0^2 xf(x)\,dx.$

However, since f(x) has different forms for $0 \le x \le 1$ and $1 < x \le 2$, we have

$$E(X) = \int_0^1 x^2\,dx + \int_1^2 (2x - x^2)\,dx$$

$$= \left[\dfrac{1}{3}x^3\right]_0^1 + \left[x^2 - \dfrac{1}{3}x^3\right]_1^2 = \dfrac{1}{3} + \left(4 - \dfrac{8}{3} - 1 + \dfrac{1}{3}\right) = 1.$$

[The result $E(X) = 1$ also follows immediately on noting that the function f(x) is symmetrical about $x = 1$, which is easily verified on drawing the graph of f(x). In general, if a probability density function f(x) is symmetrical about $x = \mu$ then it may be assumed that $E(X) = \mu$.]

$$E(X^2) = \int_0^1 x^3\,dx + \int_1^2 (2x^2 - x^3)\,dx$$

$$= \left[\dfrac{1}{4}x^4\right]_0^1 + \left[\dfrac{2}{3}x^3 - \dfrac{1}{4}x^4\right]_1^2 = \dfrac{1}{4} + \left(\dfrac{16}{3} - 4 - \dfrac{2}{3} + \dfrac{1}{4}\right) = \dfrac{14}{12}.$$

Therefore, $\quad Var(X) = E(X^2) - [E(X)]^2 = \dfrac{14}{12} - (1)^2 = \dfrac{1}{6}.$

Exercise 1.4

1. The continuous random variable X is distributed with probability density function f, where
   $$f(x) = \frac{1}{4}x^3, \quad \text{for } 0 \leq x \leq 2$$

(a) Find the mean and the variance of X.

(b) Deduce the mean and the variance of (i) $Y = 3X - 1$, (ii) $Z = 5(2 - X)$.

(c) Find the mean and the variance of $W = X(2 - X)$.

2. The continuous random variable X has probability density function f, where
   $$f(x) = \frac{5}{8}(1 - x^4), \quad \text{for } -1 \leq x \leq 1$$

(a) Find the mean and variance of X.

(b) Deduce the mean and variance of $Y = 21X + 10$.

3. The continuous random variable X has probability density function f given by
   $$f(x) = 2(1 - x), \quad \text{for } 0 < x < 1.$$

(a) Obtain an expression for $E(X^r)$, where r is a positive integer. Hence find the mean and variance of X.

(b) A rectangle is constructed with adjacent sides x cm and $(3 - 2x)$ cm, where x is a randomly observed value of X. Find the expected value of (i) the perimeter and (ii) the area of the rectangle.

4. The continuous random variable X has probability density function f given by
   $$f(x) = cx(a - x), \quad \text{for } 0 \leq x \leq 2,$$
   where c and a (≥ 2) are constants. Given that $E(X) = 1$, find
   (a) the values of c and a, (b) Var (X).

5. The random variable X is distributed with probability density function f, where
   $$f(x) = ax(1 - bx^2), \quad \text{for } 0 \leq x \leq 1.$$
   Show that b must be ≤ 1 and that $a = 4/(2 - b)$. Assuming that $b = 1$, find the mean and variance of X.

6. Find the mean and the variance of the distribution whose probability density function f is defined by
   $$f(x) = kx^3, \qquad \text{for } 0 \leq x < 1,$$
   $$f(x) = k, \qquad \text{for } 1 \leq x \leq 2.$$

7. The mass, in g, of a certain ingredient contained in 1 kg of raw material is a continuous random variable X having probability density function f where
   $$f(x) = cx, \qquad \text{for } 0 < x \leq 5,$$
   $$f(x) = c(10 - x) \qquad \text{for } 5 < x \leq 10.$$

(a)   Find the value of the constant c.

(b)   Find the mean and variance of X.

(c)   The cost of extracting the ingredient from 1 kg of the raw material is £2 if $0 < X \le 3$, is £4 if $3 < X \le 6$, and is £5 if $6 < x \le 10$. Calculate the expected cost of extracting the ingredient per kg of the raw material.

8.   The continuous random variable X has probability density function f given by

$$f(x) = a, \qquad \text{for } 0 < x < 1,$$
$$f(x) = b(4 - x), \qquad \text{for } 1 \le x \le 4,$$

where a and b are constants. Given that the mean of the distribution is 1.4, find the values of a and b.

9.   Find the mean and the variance of the distribution whose probability density function f is given by

$$f(x) = \frac{1}{4}(2 - x), \qquad \text{for } 0 \le x < 1,$$

$$f(x) = \frac{1}{4}, \qquad \text{for } 1 \le x < 2,$$

$$f(x) = \frac{1}{4}(x - 1), \qquad \text{for } 2 \le x \le 3.$$

10.   A quality characteristic X of a manufactured item is a continuous random variable having probability density function f given by

$$f(x) = \frac{2x}{\lambda^2}, \qquad \text{for } 0 < x < \lambda,$$

where λ is a positive constant whose value may be controlled by the manufacturer.

(a)   Find the mean and the variance of X in terms of λ.

(b)   Every manufactured item is inspected before being dispatched for sale. Any item for which X is 8 or more is passed for selling and any item for which X is less than 8 is scrapped. The manufacturer makes a profit of £$(27 - \lambda)$ on every item passed for selling, and suffers a loss of £$(\lambda + 5)$ on every item that is scrapped. Find the value of λ which the manufacturer should aim for in order to maximise his expected profit per item, and calculate the maximum expected profit per item.

1.5 The uniform distribution

Consider the random variable X with possible values $a \le x \le b$ and is such that an observed value of X is equally likely to be any value in the range $a \le x \le b$. Using the analogy introduced in Section 1.1 of regarding the one unit of probability as powder in a jug, then it is clear that the probability should be distributed uniformly (evenly) over the interval [a, b] as shown in the following diagram. Since the 'mound', in this case a rectangle, is of unit area, it follows that the height of the rectangle must be $1/(b - a)$.

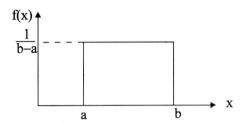

Thus, the probability density function f is given by

$$f(x) = \frac{1}{b-a}, \qquad \text{for } a \le x \le b \tag{1}$$

A random variable having this probability density function is said to have the **uniform** distribution over the interval [a, b], which we shall abbreviate as $X \sim U(a, b)$.

As a simple example of how such a random variable may arise in practice, suppose that a string of length 10 cm is to be cut into two pieces, the cutting point being chosen at random. Let X cm denote the distance of the cutting point from one end of the string. Then X has the possible values $0 < x < 10$ and all these values are equally likely, so that $X \sim U(0, 10)$.

If $X \sim U(a, b)$, then the cumulative distribution function F is given by

$$
\begin{aligned}
F(x) &= 0, & \text{for } x < a, \\
F(x) &= \frac{x-a}{b-a}, & \text{for } a \le x \le b \\
F(x) &= 1, & \text{for } x > b.
\end{aligned}
\tag{2}
$$

In particular, note that for any subinterval [c, d] of (a, b)

$$P(c \le X \le d) \equiv F(d) - F(c) = \frac{d-c}{b-a}, \tag{3}$$

so that the probability that X will take a value in any subinterval is directly proportional to the width of the subinterval.

Mean and variance

The mean of the distribution U(a, b) is

$$E(X) = \frac{1}{b-a}\int_a^b x\,dx = \frac{1}{b-a}\left[\frac{1}{2}x^2\right]_a^b = \frac{b^2 - a^2}{2(b-a)} = \frac{1}{2}(b+a) \tag{4}$$

which is also evident on noting that f(x) is symmetrical about $x = \frac{1}{2}(b+a)$.

$$E(X^2) = \frac{1}{b-a}\int_a^b x^2\,dx = \frac{1}{b-a}\left[\frac{1}{3}x^3\right]_a^b = \frac{b^3 - a^3}{3(b-a)} = \frac{1}{3}(b^2 + ba + a^2)$$

on noting that $(b^3 - a^3) = (b-a)(b^2 + ba + a^2)$.

It follows that the variance of U(a, b) is

$$\text{Var}(X) = E(X^2) - [E(X)]^2 = \frac{1}{3}(b^2 + ba + a^2) - \frac{1}{4}(b+a)^2 = \frac{1}{12}(b-a)^2.$$

Example 1

A string of length 10 cm is cut at a randomly chosen point.

(a) Find the probability that the length of the longer piece will be more than 7 cm.

(b) Find the expected length of the longer piece.

Let X denote the distance in cm of the cutting point from one end of the string. Then X ~ U(0, 10) and its probability density function is

$$f(x) = 0.1, \qquad \text{for } 0 < x < 10.$$

Solution

(a) The lengths of the two pieces in cm are X and (10 − X). Let A denote the event that the length of the longer piece exceeds 7 cm. Then allowing for either piece being more than 7 cm long we have

$$A = (X > 7) \cup (10 - X > 7) = (X > 7) \cup (X < 3).$$

Therefore,
$$P(A) = P(X > 7) + P(X < 3) = \frac{10-7}{10} + \frac{3-0}{10} = 0.6.$$

(b) Let Y denote the length in cm of the longer piece. Then

$$Y = X \quad \text{if } X > 5,$$
$$Y = 10 - X \quad \text{if } X < 5.$$

Hence
$$E(Y) = 0.1 \int_0^5 (10 - x)\,dx + 0.1 \int_5^{10} x\,dx$$

$$= 0.1\left[10x - \frac{1}{2}x^2\right]_0^5 + 0.1\left[\frac{1}{2}x^2\right]_5^{10}$$

$$= 0.1 \times \frac{75}{2} + 0.1 \times \frac{75}{2} = 7.5.$$

So, the expected length of the longer piece is 7.5 cm.

Example 2

In the quadratic equation in u given by

$$u^2 - 2u - X = 0,$$

the value X is chosen at random from the interval (−1, 1). Calculate the probability that the larger root of the equation will be less than 1.5.

Solution

The roots of the equation are

$$\frac{2 \pm \sqrt{4 + 4X}}{2} = 1 \pm \sqrt{(1+X)},$$

the larger one being $Y = 1 + \sqrt{(1+X)}$.

$$P(Y < 1.5) = P(1 + \sqrt{(1+X)} < 1.5) = P(1 + X < 0.25) = P(X < -0.75).$$

But $X \sim U(-1, 1)$ and therefore, by (3)

$$P(X < -0.75) = \frac{-0.75 - (-1)}{1 - (-1)} = \frac{0.25}{2} = 0.125.$$

Exercise 1.5

1. In each of the following evaluate (i) $P(3 < X < 5)$, (ii) $E(X)$, (iii) $Var(X)$.
   (a) $X \sim U(2, 10)$, (b) $X \sim U(-2, 8)$.

2. The random variable X is uniformly distributed over the interval $(0, 8)$.
   If $Y = X^{1/3}$, evaluate (a) $P(Y > 1)$ and (b) $E(Y)$.

3. A square has each side of length X cm, where $X \sim U(4, 10)$. Find the mean and the variance of the area of the square.

4. A rectangle of perimeter 16 cm has one side of length X cm, where X is uniformly distributed over the interval $(3, 7)$. If Y cm^2 is the area of the rectangle find
   (a) the mean value of Y, (b) $P(Y > 12)$.

5. A string of length 12 cm is cut at a point chosen at random. Let Y cm^2 denote the area of the rectangle, two of whose sides are formed by the two pieces of the string. Evaluate (a) the expected value of Y, (b) $P(Y > 20)$.

6. AB is the diameter of a semicircle of radius r. AP is a chord making an angle X radians with AB, where $X \sim U(0, \pi/2)$. Find the expected value of the area of the triangle APB.

7. A tank with vertical faces has a horizontal rectangular base with sides X m and $(10 - X)$ m, where X is uniformly distributed over $(6, 9)$. The tank contains 100 m^3 of water. Calculate, to three decimal places, the probability that the depth of water in the tank exceeds 5 m.

8. In the quadratic equation $y^2 - 2Xy + X + 2 = 0$, the value of X is chosen at random from the interval $(-5, 5)$. Calculate the probability that the equation will have real roots.
   If, instead, the value of X is chosen at random from the interval $(2, 5)$, calculate the probability that the smaller root will be less than 1.

1.6 The normal distribution

Introduction

In this section we introduce a continuous distribution which is the most widely used one in Statistics and will figure prominently in the applications covered later. Despite the fact that a random variable having this distribution has possible values ranging from $-\infty$ to $+\infty$, the distribution has been found to be a reasonable model in practice. It arises mainly when an observed value of a random variable is dependent on several factors. For example, heights of adults (male or female) and errors of measurement are such variables. The histogram from a very large number of observations of such a variable has a shape that resembles that of the distribution to be considered here. The distribution alluded to is known as the **normal** distribution (but this should not be interpreted as implying that there is anything abnormal or peculiar about a non-normal distribution!).

Before dealing with the general form of the normal distribution which is used in practice we shall start with its standard form.

The standard normal distribution

Consider the function ϕ defined by

$$\phi(z) = \frac{1}{\sqrt{(2\pi)}} e^{-\frac{1}{2}z^2}, \qquad \text{for} -\infty < z < +\infty \qquad (1)$$

a sketch of which is shown below,

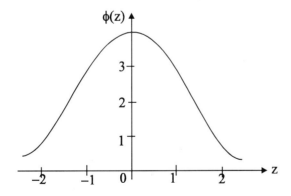

It is clear that $\phi(z)$ is > 0 for all z, and it may be shown (using mathematics beyond the level assumed in this text) that

$$\int_{-\infty}^{\infty} \phi(z)dz = 1 \qquad (2)$$

Thus, ϕ can serve as a probability density function. A random variable having ϕ as its probability density function will be denoted by Z and said to have the **standard normal distribution**. It is evident from the symmetry of $\phi(z)$ about $z = 0$ that $E(Z) = 0$. It may also be shown that $Var(Z) = 1$. We shall abbreviate this information by writing $Z \sim N(0,1)$ to indicate that the random variable Z has the standard normal distribution with probability density function ϕ given by (1). The cumulative distribution function Φ of Z is given by

$$P(Z \le z) \;=\; \Phi(z) \;=\; \int_{-\infty}^{z} \phi(t)dt \;=\; \frac{1}{\sqrt{(2\pi)}} \int_{-\infty}^{z} e^{-\frac{1}{2}t^2} dt \tag{3}$$

In view of the symmetry of $\phi(z)$ about $z = 0$, it follows that $\Phi(0) = 0.5$. However, for any $z \ne 0$, $\Phi(z)$ can only be evaluated using numerical methods. The results of such numerical evaluations have been tabulated extensively. Table 3 of the RND tables gives the values of $P(Z \le z) \equiv \Phi(z)$ to five decimal places for values of z from 0 to 3.99 in steps of 0.01. Table 3 of Murdoch and Barnes gives the values of $P(Z > z) \equiv 1 - \Phi(z)$ to four decimal places for values of z from 0 to 2.99 in steps of 0.01, and for z from 3.0 to 4.0 in steps of 0.1. Future reference to these sets of tables will be abbreviated to RND and M&B.

What if z is negative? For a negative z we can make use of the symmetry of $\phi(z)$ about $z = 0$. As illustrated in the following diagram, for any $a > 0$,

$$P(Z < -a) \;=\; P(Z > a) \;=\; 1 - P(Z < a), \tag{4a}$$

and similarly,

$$P(Z > -a) \;=\; P(Z < a) \;=\; 1 - P(Z > a). \tag{4b}$$

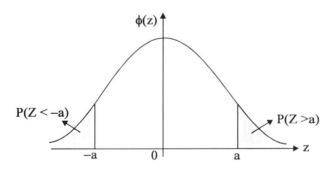

The following example illustrates the use of tables for evaluating probabilities of events of the form $(a < Z < b)$. The given solutions are based on a table of values of $P(Z < z)$ as given in Table 3 of RND. The solutions will need to be modified appropriately if the tables used gives the values of $P(Z > z)$ as in Table 3 of M&B.

Example 1

Given that Z ~ N(0, 1) use tables to evaluate correct to three decimal places

(a) P(Z < 0.5),   (b) P(Z > 1.66),   (c) P(Z < −0.5),   (d) P(Z > − 2.6),

(e) P(1.24 < Z < 2.36),   (f) P(− 1.23 < Z < 1.89)

Solution

(a) From Table 3 we have P(Z < 0.5) = 0.69146 = 0.691 to 3 decimal places.

(b)   P(Z > 1.66) = 1 − P(Z < 1.66) = 1 − 0.95154 = 0.048 to 3 decimal places.

(c) Using (4a) above,

　　　　P(Z < −0.5) = 1 − P(Z < 0.5) = 1 − 0.69146 = 0.309 to 3 decimal places.

(d) Using (4b) above,

　　　　P(Z > − 2.6)   = P(Z < 2.6) = 0.99534 = 0.995 to 3 decimal places.

(e) P(1.24 < Z < 2.36) = P(Z < 2.36) − P(Z < 1.24) = 0.99086 − 0.89251

　　　　　　　　　　　　　　　　　　　　　　　= 0.098 to 3 decimal places.

(f) P(−1.23 < Z < 1.89) = P(Z < 1.89) − P(Z < − 1.23)

　　　　　　　　　　= P(Z < 1.89) − [1 − P(Z < 1.23)]   on using (4a)

　　　　　　　　　　= 0.97062 − (1 − 0.89065)   = 0.861 to 3 decimal places.

[To avoid errors which occur fairly often it pays to draw a diagram showing the area that is required and, in particular, to assess whether the answer is greater than or less than 0.5].

To evaluate P(Z > a) or P(Z < a) when a is given to more than two decimal places we would need to use linear interpolation in Table 3 of RND or M&B. However, in this text we shall round a to two decimal places and accept the answer obtained as being of sufficient accuracy. In so doing, the errors arising decrease as a (> 0) increases. In the vast majority of cases the answer will be correct to at least two decimal places.

For example,

　　　　P(Z < 2.6746) ≈ P(Z < 2.67) = 0.99621 = 0.996 to 3 decimal places.

As it happens this particular answer is the value of P(Z < 2.6746) correct to three decimal places, since both P(Z < 2.67) and P(Z < 2.68) equal 0.996 to three decimal places.

Now consider P(Z < 0.2672),

　　　　P(Z < 0.2672) ≈ P(Z < 0.27) = 0.60642 = 0.606 to 3 decimal places.

In this case linear interpolation in Table 3 would give the answer 0.6053 to four decimal places, so that our approximation is correct to only two decimal places.

In some problems we shall need to find a such that $P(Z < a) = p$ for some given value of p between 0 and 1. Note that a will be negative if $p < 0.5$ and positive if $p > 0.5$. The solution for any given p can be obtained by linear interpolation in Table 3 but it is much easier to use Table 4 in RND or M&B. Table 4 of RND gives the values of z to three decimal places for which $P(Z \leq z) = p$ for selected values of $p > 0.5$, while Table 4 of M&B gives the values of z to four decimal places for which $P(Z > z) = p$ for selected values of $p < 0.5$.

The use of Table 4 in RND is illustrated in the following example. The solutions will need to be modified appropriately if M&B is used.

Example 2

Given that $Z \sim N(0, 1)$ find a in each of the following cases giving the answer correct to two decimal places, (a) $P(Z < a) = 0.992$, (b) $P(Z < a) = 0.35$.

Solution

(a) Directly from Table 4 we find that $P(Z < a) = 0.992$ has the solution $a = 2.409$.

(b) It is clear that the value of a such that $P(Z < a) = 0.35$ is negative. Now

$$P(Z < a) = P(Z > -a) = 1 - P(Z < -a).$$

Thus, $P(Z < a) = 0.35$ is equivalent to $1 - P(Z < -a) = 0.35$, or $P(Z < -a) = 0.65$. From Table 4 we find that $-a = 0.385$, so that $a = -0.385$.

Exercise 1.6a

Assuming that $Z \sim N(0, 1)$ evaluate to two decimal places

1. $P(Z < 1.95)$,   2. $P(Z > 1.06)$,   3. $P(Z > -2.16)$,   4. $P(Z > -0.08)$,
5. $P(1.24 < Z < 2.34)$ 6. $P(Z > 0.9887)$,   7. $P(Z < -1.843)$,
8. $P(2.04 < Z < 2.98)$,   9. $P(-1.067 < Z < -0.093)$,   10. c if $P(Z < c) = 0.982$,
11. c if $P(Z > c) = 0.03$,   12. c if $P(Z < c) = 0.027$

The General Normal Distribution

We now extend the standard normal distribution to one which may serve as a model for a wide range of random variables.

Let $X = \mu + \sigma Z$. Then, using results given in Section 1.4,

$$E(X) = \mu + \sigma E(Z) = \mu, \text{ since } E(Z) = 0,$$

and $\qquad$ $\text{Var}(X) = \sigma^2 \text{Var}(Z) = \sigma^2, \text{ since } \text{Var}(Z) = 1.$

It follows that the distribution of X has mean μ and variance σ^2. Furthermore, it may be shown that the probability density function f of X is given by

$$f(x) = \frac{1}{\sigma\sqrt{2\pi}} e^{-(x-\mu)^2/(2\sigma^2)}, \qquad \text{for } -\infty < x < \infty. \qquad (5)$$

Conversely, the transformation $Z = (X - \mu)/\sigma$ will reduce f to ϕ. A random variable X having the probability density function f given in (5) is said to have the **normal distribution** with mean μ and variance σ^2, which we abbreviate as $X \sim N(\mu, \sigma^2)$. The transformation $Z = (X - \mu)/\sigma$ enables us to reduce any $N(\mu, \sigma^2)$ to $N(0, 1)$. This is illustrated in the following examples.

Example 3

Given that X is normally distributed with mean 5 and standard deviation 2, evaluate

(a) $P(X < 6)$,   (b) $P(X < 2.56)$,   (c) $P(3.4 < X < 5.7)$,   (d) c such that $P(X < c) = 0.63$.

Solution

From the above we know that $Z = (X - 5)/2$ has the distribution $N(0,1)$.

(a) $\qquad P(X < 6) \;=\; P\left(Z < \dfrac{6-5}{2}\right) \;=\; P(Z < 0.5)$

$\qquad\qquad\qquad\qquad = 0.69146 = 0.691$ to 3 decimal places.

(b) $\qquad P(X < 2.56) \;=\; P\left(Z < \dfrac{2.56-5}{2}\right) \;=\; P(Z < -1.22) \;=\; 1 - P(Z < 1.22)$

$\qquad\qquad\qquad\qquad = 1 - 0.88877 = 0.111 \quad$ to 3 decimal places.

(c) $\quad P(3.4 < X < 5.7) = P\left(\dfrac{3.4-5}{2} < Z < \dfrac{5.7-5}{2}\right) \;=\; P(-0.8 < Z < 0.35)$

$\qquad\qquad\qquad\qquad = P(Z < 0.35) - P(Z < -0.8) \;=\; P(Z < 0.35) - [1 - P(Z < 0.8)]$

$\qquad\qquad\qquad\qquad = 0.63683 - (1 - 0.78814) = 0.425$ to 3 decimal places.

(d) $\qquad P(X < c) \;=\; P\left(Z < \dfrac{c-5}{2}\right)$

Using Table 4

$\qquad P\left(Z < \dfrac{c-5}{2}\right) \;=\; 0.63 \text{ when } \dfrac{c-5}{2} = 0.332$

Hence, $\qquad c \;=\; 2 \times 0.332 + 5 \;=\; 5.664.$

Example 4

A machine produces cylindrical rods whose diameters are normally distributed with mean 1 cm and standard deviation 0.01 cm. A rod is satisfactory for a specific purpose only if its diameter lies between 0.993 cm and 1.017 cm.

(a) Find the probability that a randomly chosen rod will be satisfactory.

(b) Given that a rod has a diameter greater than 1 cm find, correct to three significant figures, the probability that the rod is satisfactory.

(c) Find, correct to three significant figures, the mean value of the cross-sectional areas of the rods.

Solution

Let X cm denote the diameter of a randomly chosen rod. Then $X \sim N(1, 0.01^2)$, and

$$Z = \frac{X-1}{0.01} \sim N(0, 1)$$

(a) P(rod is satisfactory) $= P(0.993 < X < 1.017)$

$$= P\left(\frac{0.993-1}{0.01} < Z < \frac{1.017-1}{0.01}\right) = P(Z < 1.7) - P(Z < -0.7)$$

$$= 0.95543 - (1 - 0.75804) = 0.7135 \text{ to 4 decimal places.}$$

(b) P(rod is satisfactory | X > 1) $= P(0.993 < X < 1.017 \,|\, X > 1) = \dfrac{P(1 < X < 1.017)}{P(X > 1)}$

$$P(1 < X < 1.017) = P\left(\frac{1-1}{0.01} < Z < \frac{1.017-1}{0.01}\right) = P(Z < 1.7) - P(Z < 0)$$

$$= 0.95543 - 0.5 = 0.45543.$$

$$P(X > 1) = P\left(Z > \frac{1-1}{0.01}\right) = P(Z > 0) = 0.5$$

Hence, P(rod is satisfactory | X > 1) $= \dfrac{0.45543}{0.5} = 0.911$ to 3 significant figures.

(c) Let Y cm^2 denote the cross-sectional area of a rod of diameter X cm. Then
$Y = \frac{1}{4}\pi X^2$. The mean cross-sectional area is $E(Y) = \frac{\pi}{4}E(X^2)$.

Since $X \sim N(1, 0.01^2)$, $E(X) = 1$ and $\text{Var}(X) = 0.01^2$. Therefore

$$E(X^2) = \text{Var}(X) + [E(X)]^2 = 0.01^2 + 1 = 1.0001.$$

The mean cross-sectional area of the rods is $\dfrac{1.0001\pi}{4} = 0.785$ cm^2 to 3 significant

figures.

[Since the diameter of a rod cannot possibly be negative it might appear strange to be using a normal distribution (defined form $-\infty$ to $+\infty$) as the model for the distribution of the diameters of the rods. However, under this model the probability that the diameter of a rod will be negative is

$$P(X < 0) = P\left(Z < \frac{0-1}{0.01}\right) = P(Z < -100) \quad \text{which is negligibly small.}]$$

Example 5

The heights, in metres, of adult males may be assumed to be normally distributed. Given that 10% of adult males are taller than 1.8 metres and that 5% are shorter than 1.6 metres, find the mean and the standard deviation of the heights of adult males.

Solution

Let X metres denote the height of a randomly chosen adult male. We are assuming that

$$X \sim N(\mu, \sigma^2),$$

where μ and σ are to be determined given that

$$P(X > 1.8) = 0.1 \quad \text{and} \quad P(X < 1.6) = 0.05.$$

Standardising we have

$$P\left(Z > \frac{1.8 - \mu}{\sigma}\right) = 0.1 \quad \text{and} \quad P\left(Z < \frac{1.6 - \mu}{\sigma}\right) = 0.05.$$

Using Table 4 of RND we have

$$\frac{1.8 - \mu}{\sigma} = 1.282 \quad \text{and} \quad \frac{1.6 - \mu}{\sigma} = -1.645,$$

leading to $\quad 1.8 - \mu = 1.282\sigma \quad$ and $\quad 1.6 - \mu = -1.645\sigma.$

Subtracting these two equations gives

$$0.2 = 2.927\sigma, \text{ so that } \sigma = \frac{0.2}{2.927} \approx 0.0683.$$

Eliminating σ from the two equations by taking their ratio we have

$$\frac{1.8 - \mu}{1.6 - \mu} = -\frac{1.282}{1.645} \text{ or } 1.645(1.8 - \mu) = -1.282(1.6 - \mu)$$

from which it follows that

$$\mu = \frac{1.645 \times 1.8 + 1.282 \times 1.6}{1.645 + 1.282} = 1.7124$$

Thus, to three decimal places, the heights of male adults have mean 1.712 m and standard deviation 0.068 m.

Exercise 1.6b

1.   Given that X is normally distributed with mean 2 and standard deviation 1,

(a)   evaluate to three decimal places (i) $P(X < 2)$, (ii) $P(X < 3.65)$, (iii) $P(X > 2.07)$, (iv) $P(0 < X < 3)$, (v) $P(1.56 < X < 2.54)$.

(b)   find c, to three significant figures, in each of the cases where (i) $P(X > c) = 0.005$, (ii) $P(X < c) = 0.1$.

2.   Given that X is normally distributed with mean 2.86 and standard deviation 1.2, find the values of

(a) $P(X < 3.7)$, (b) $P(X > 1.72)$, (c) $P(3.1 < X < 3.4)$, (d) $P(1.66 < X < 2.98)$.

3.   Suppose that the time X that an athlete takes to run 1500 m is normally distributed with mean 4 minutes and standard deviation 20 seconds. Calculate the probability

that this athlete will run 1500 m in (a) less than 4 minutes, (b) less than 3.25 minutes, (c) in a time somewhere between 3.9 minutes and 4.2 minutes.

4.   A weighing device is such that the recorded weights in repeated weighings of an object are normally distributed with mean equal to the true weight of the object and standard deviation 0.02 g. If the device is used once to weigh an object whose true weight is 10 g, calculate the probability that the recorded weight will be in the range from 9.99 g to 10.02 g.

5.   Two electronic devices A and B have life-lengths in months of X and Y respectively, where $X \sim N(40, 6^2)$ and $Y \sim N(45, 3^2)$. Determine which of the two devices is the more likely to last (a) at least 48 months, (b) at least 52 months.

6.   Large scale testing by means of a standardised test on children of a certain age-group gave scores whose distribution could be modelled by a normal distribution with mean 74 and standard deviation 15. This test is recommended for grading purposes and the following system is adopted. The top grade 'A' is to be awarded to 10% of the candidates, the next highest grade 'B' to 30% of the candidates, the third highest grade 'C' to 40% of the candidates, and the lowest grade 'D' to the remaining 20% of the candidates. Determine the range of scores for each grade.

7.   The error made by a certain length-measuring instrument is known to be normally distributed with mean zero and standard deviation 0.5 mm. Find the probability that the error in a measurement will be (a) **numerically** greater than 1 mm, (b) **numerically** greater than 0.5 mm.

8.   The operational lifetimes in hours of manufactured light bulbs are normally distributed with mean 1060. Find, to two decimal places, the standard deviation of the lifetimes given that 80% of the bulbs have lifetimes exceeding 1050 hours.

9.   The inside diameter of a nozzle has a normal distribution with mean 4 cm and standard deviation 0.1 cm. The specification for the inside diameter of a nozzle is 4 cm. If the inside diameter of a nozzle differs from specification by more than 0.05 cm but less than 0.08 cm, then the loss to the manufacturer is 50 pence. If the inside diameter of a nozzle differs from specification by more than 0.08 cm then the loss to the manufacturer is £1. The manufacturer makes a profit of £2 on each

nozzle whose inside diameter is within 0.05 cm of specification. Find, to the nearest penny, the manufacturer's expected profit per nozzle.

10. An automatic filling device is used for putting liquid into containers. When the device is set to put μ cm^3 into each container the actual volume put in a container is normally distributed with mean μ cm^3 and standard deviation 0.1 cm^3. (a) If the device is set to put 12 cm^3 into each container, calculate correct to two decimal places, the proportion of the containers that will contain between 11.8 cm^3 and 12.1 cm^3. (b) Find, to two decimal places, the value of μ that should be set if it is required that only 10% of the containers will contain less than 12 cm^3 of liquid.

11. A man makes the same journey to work each day. The time at which his work starts is 08.30. If he leaves home at 07.30 he is late 5% of the time, while if he leaves home at 07.25 he is late only 1% of the time. Assuming that the times he takes to get to work are normally distributed with the same mean and standard deviation irrespective of the starting times, calculate the mean and the standard deviation.

12. A certain ingredient is extracted from raw material using either of two methods A and B. For a fixed volume of raw material the amount X cm^3 of ingredient extracted using method A is normally distributed with mean 13 and standard deviation 2. The amount Y cm^3 extracted using method B is distributed with probability density function f given by
$$f(y) = 0.08(y - 10), \text{ for } 10 \le y \le 15.$$
Determine which of the two methods (a) has the greater probability of extracting more than 14 cm^3, (b) extracts the greater amount on average.
The cost of applying method A is 3 pence per cm^3 extracted and that of applying method B is $(15 + 2Y)$ pence. (c) If the extracted ingredient is sold at 5 pence per cm^3, determine which of the two methods gives the higher expected profit.

13. In a certain examination the marks obtained were found to be normally distributed with mean 42 and standard deviation 10. For a specific purpose it was required to transform these marks so that the mean would be 50 and the standard deviation would be 15. Derive the necessary transformation and determine the new mark corresponding to an original mark of 40.

14.   The time taken by a postwoman to deliver mail to a particular housing estate is normally distributed with mean 12 minutes and standard deviation 2 minutes. Assuming that in a year she delivers mail to this estate on 300 days, estimate the number of days that she takes (a) longer than 17 minutes, (b) less than 10 minutes, (c) between 10 and 15 minutes.

15.   The masses of articles produced in a certain factory are known to be normally distributed. Given that 5% of the articles have a mass exceeding 85 g and 10% have a mass below 25 g, find the mean and the standard deviation of the masses of the articles.

16.   The bearings produced at a certain factory have diameters that are normally distributed with mean 14.2 mm and standard deviation 1.2 mm. (a)   Find the probability that a randomly chosen bearing will have a diameter less than 13.9 mm. (b)   Six bearings are chosen at random.   Find, to two significant figures, the probability that at least five of the six bearings will have diameters in the range from 13.9 mm to 14.5 mm.

17.   The breaking strength X kg of a rope is normally distributed with mean 100 and standard deviation 4. Each coil of the rope is sold at a profit of £25 if $X > 95$, but if $X \leq 95$ the coil has to be sold for a different purpose at a profit of £10. Calculate the expected profit per coil.

18.   The amount of liquid delivered per cup by a drinks machine is normally distributed with mean 200 ml and standard deviation 8 ml. (a)   Given that the maximum capacity of a cup is 210 ml calculate the proportion of cups that will overflow. (b) Find, to the nearest ml, the maximum capacity a cup should have if only 1% of the cups are to overflow.

1.7 Normal Approximations to Binomial and Poisson Distributions

We have seen how the existence of tables simplifies the task of evaluating probabilities of events associated with a normal distribution.   When the probability of some event associated with a non-normal distribution is difficult or time-consuming to evaluate, it would be worth looking at the possibility of approximating the distribution by a normal distribution and using it to find an approximate value for the probability.   Since the normal distribution is bell-shaped and symmetrical it will serve as an approximation only to a distribution that is roughly bell-shaped and symmetrical or nearly symmetrical. The normal distribution to use is the one having mean and variance equal to those of the distribution being approximated. As an example, suppose that X ~ B(200, 0.6) and we wish to evaluate P(X ≤ 100). Without access to a table or computer programme of binomial probabilities for n = 200 and p = 0.6 we are faced with a daunting task. We shall see that in this example a reasonable approximate value for the probability can be obtained by assuming that the distribution of X is approximately normal with mean equal to 200 × 0.6 = 120 and variance equal to 120 × 0.4 = 48.

We shall also consider a normal approximation for evaluating Poisson probabilities.

Before discussing the conditions under which normal approximations to binomial and Poisson distributions are appropriate, we first observe that in each case we are approximating the distribution of a discrete random variable, having possible values that are non-negative integers, by a continuous distribution. To allow for this the probability assigned to the integer k has to be spread over the interval from k − 0.5 to k + 0.5, which is referred to as the **continuity correction**. Let X denote a discrete random variable whose possible values are integers. Suppose that the distribution of X is to be approximated by the distribution of Y, where Y is a continuous random variable. Then, on applying the continuity correction we have for any integer k,

$$P(X = k) \approx P(k - 0.5 < Y < k + 0.5),$$
$$P(X \leq k) \approx P(Y < k + 0.5)$$
$$P(X \geq k) \approx P(Y > k - 0.5).$$

Normal Approximation to a Binomial Distribution

As indicated above a normal approximation to B(n, p) will be reasonable only when the distribution B(n, p) is symmetrical or approximately so. The B(n, p) distribution is symmetrical for p = 0.5, so that when p = 0.5 a normal approximation will be appropriate. Since the normal distribution extends from − ∞ to + ∞ but B(n, 0.5) extends from 0 to n, it follows that the larger the value of n the better the approximation will be. For any p ≠ 0.5 the larger the value of n the more nearly symmetrical will be the distribution B(n, p); thus, the further p deviates from 0.5 the larger will n need to be for the normal approximation to be reasonably good. It is not possible to formulate a rule on the values of n and p for which a normal approximation is reasonable. A useful guideline is based on the need for the bulk of the normal distribution to be in the interval [0, n], which is the range of values of the binomial B(n, p). For the N(μ, σ^2) distribution we can verify from tables that the interval [μ − 4σ, μ + 4σ] has probability 0.99994, which is close enough to

1 for practical purposes. Since our normal approximation has mean np and variance npq, this suggests that we should have

$$np - 4\sqrt{npq} > 0 \text{ and } np + 4\sqrt{npq} < n,$$

from which it follows that n should be greater than the larger of 16p/q and 16q/p.

Thus, a simple rule of thumb for determining whether a normal approximation to B(n, p) is reasonable is to check that

$$n > \max\left(\frac{16p}{q}, \frac{16q}{p}\right).$$

Consider B(200, 0.6). We have

$$\frac{16p}{q} = 16 \times \frac{0.6}{0.4} = 24 \text{ and } \frac{16q}{p} = 16 \times \frac{0.4}{0.6} = 10.67.$$

In this case n = 200 is very much larger than 24 so that the normal approximation should be good.

Example 1

If X ~ B(200, 0.6) find approximate values for

(a) P(X = 110),   (b) P(X ≥ 100),   (c) P(120 < X < 140).

Solution

B(200, 0.6) has mean 200 × 0.6 = 120 and variance 120 × 0.4 = 48. Let Y ~ N(120, 48), which will be our normal approximation to B(200, 0.6).

(a) On applying the continuity correction, P(X = 110) ≡ P(109.5 < X < 110.5).

$$P(X = 110) \approx P(109.5 < Y < 110.5)$$

$$= P\left(\frac{109.5 - 120}{\sqrt{48}} < Z < \frac{110.5 - 120}{\sqrt{48}}\right)$$

$$\approx P(-1.52 < Z < -1.37)$$

$$= P(1.37 < Z < 1.52) \text{ on using the symmetry of N(0, 1),}$$

$$= P(Z < 1.52) - P(Z < 1.37) = 0.93574 - 0.91466$$

$$= 0.021 \text{ to 3 decimal places.}$$

[The binomial probability is 0.0202 correct to 4 decimal places.]

(b) $$P(X \geq 100) \equiv P(X > 99.5) \approx P(Y > 99.5)$$

$$= P\left(Z > \frac{99.5 - 120}{\sqrt{48}}\right) \approx P(Z > -2.96) = P(Z < 2.96)$$

$$= 0.99846 = 0.998 \text{ to 3 decimal places.}$$

[The binomial probability is 0.9983 correct to 4 decimal places.]

(c) $P(120 < X < 140) \equiv P(121 \le X \le 139) \equiv P(120.5 < X < 139.5)$

$\approx P(120.5 < Y < 139.5)$

$= P\left(\dfrac{120.5 - 120}{\sqrt{48}} < Z < \dfrac{139.5 - 120}{\sqrt{48}}\right) \approx P(0.07 < Z < 2.81)$

$= P(Z < 2.81) - P(Z < 0.07)$

$= 0.99752 - 0.52790 = 0.470$ to 3 decimal places.

[The binomial probability is 0.4710 correct to 4 decimal places.]

Exercise 1.7a

1.   If $X \sim B(20, 0.5)$ use a normal distribution to find approximate values for

(a) $P(X = 11)$,   (b) $P(X \le 15)$,   (c) $P(7 \le X \le 15)$. Compare your approximations with the exact probabilities obtained using Table 1 (in RND or M&B).

2.   If $X \sim B(50, 0.4)$ use a normal distribution to find approximate values for

(a) $P(X = 19)$,   (b) $P(X \le 24)$,   (c) $P(18 \le X \le 25)$. Compare your approximations with the exact probabilities obtained using Table 1 (in RND or M&B).

3.   Find an approximate value for the probability of obtaining at least 50 heads in 120 tosses of a fair coin.

4.   The random variable X has the distribution $B(n, p)$.   Using appropriate approximations **when necessary** evaluate $P(X = np)$ in each of the cases when

(a) $n = 400, p = 0.5$,   (b) $n = 550, p = 0.8$,   (c) $n = 50, p = 0.8$.

5.   Two fair dice are to be thrown together 180 times. Find an approximate value for the probability that in at least 25 of the throws the sum of the two scores will be 7.

6.   An electronic device consists of 120 components and it will function throughout a given time period only if at least 100 of the components do not fail during the time period.

Independently for each component the probability is 0.25 that a component will fail during the time period. Find an approximate value for the probability that the device will operate throughout the time period.

7.   Of the population of England and Wales, 22% have blood group A. In a random sample of 150 people, find an approximate value for the probability that the number of blood group A in the sample is (a) 20 or fewer, (b) 30 or more.

8.   The probability that a child is left-handed is 0.2. For a school of 1600 children use a normal approximation to find the probability that the number of left-handed children in the school will be between 330 and 350, both inclusive.

9.   It is known that 35% of children will be absent from school on at least one day during a term. Use a normal distribution to find approximate values for the

probabilities that in a sample of 400 children the number absent from school on at least one day next term will be (a) fewer than 120, (b) between 120 and 150 inclusive, (c) more than 160.

10. A certain variety of flower seed is sold in packets, each packet containing 150 seeds. It is known that 40% of such seeds will germinate and produce white flowers. Find an approximate value for the probability that between 50 and 60 (both inclusive) of the seeds in a packet will produce white flowers.

11. In a multiple-choice test paper there are 100 questions, each with a choice of three answers only one of which is correct. To pass the test it is necessary to answer at least 40 questions correctly. Use a normal distribution to find an approximate value for the probability that a candidate who chooses the answer to each question randomly will pass the test. Also find an approximate value for the probability of such a candidate passing if the choice of answers to each question is increased to four.

Normal Approximation to a Poisson Distribution

A Poisson distribution cannot possibly be symmetrical but the larger the mean μ the more nearly symmetrical is the distribution. Since the mean and the variance of the Poisson distribution with parameter μ are both μ the appropriate normal approximating distribution will be $N(\mu, \mu)$. Since the Poisson distribution extends from 0 to ∞, the guideline rule used for the binomial distribution leads to the condition

$$\mu - 4\sqrt{\mu} > 0 \text{ or } \mu > 16.$$

Hence, a normal approximation to a Poisson distribution should be reasonable for any $\mu > 16$ and the larger the value of μ the better the approximation.

Example 2

If $X \sim Po(15)$ use Table 2 to evaluate (a) $P(X = 15)$, (b) $P(12 \leq X \leq 17)$, (c) $P(X \leq 13)$. Use a normal distribution to find approximate values for these probabilities.

Solution

(a) On using Table 2 (RND)

$$P(X = 15) \equiv P(X \leq 15) - P(X \leq 14) = 0.5681 - 0.4657 = 0.1024.$$

We use $Y \sim N(15, 15)$ as the normal approximation to the distribution of X. On applying the continuity correction we have

$$P(X = 15) \equiv P(14.5 < X < 15.5) \approx P(14.5 < Y < 15.5)$$
$$= P\left(\frac{14.5 - 15}{\sqrt{15}} < Z < \frac{15.5 - 15}{\sqrt{15}}\right) \approx P(-0.13 < Z < 0.13)$$

$$= 0.55172 - (1 - 0.55172) = 0.1034,$$

which is reasonably close to the exact value 0.1024, being correct to two decimal places.

(b) Using Table 2 we have

$$P(12 \le X \le 17) = P(X \le 17) - P(X \le 11) = 0.7489 - 0.1848 = 0.5641.$$

Using the normal approximation and the continuity correction we have

$$P(12 \le X \le 17) \equiv P(11.5 < X < 17.5) \approx P(11.5 < Y < 17.5)$$

$$= P\left(\frac{11.5 - 15}{\sqrt{15}} < Z < \frac{17.5 - 15}{\sqrt{15}}\right) \approx P(-0.90 < Z < 0.65)$$

$$= 0.74215 - (1 - 0.81594) = 0.55809,$$

which again gives an answer correct to two decimal places.

(c) Using Table 2,

$$P(X \le 13) = 0.3632.$$

Using the normal approximation and the continuity correction we have

$$P(X \le 13) \equiv P(X < 13.5) \approx P(Y < 13.5)$$

$$= P\left(Z < \frac{13.5 - 15}{\sqrt{15}}\right) \approx P(Z < -0.39)$$

$$= 1 - P(Z < 0.39) = 0.34827$$

which is the least accurate of the calculations made in this example. [But note that $\mu = 15$ is less than the minimum value indicated above for a normal approximation to be reasonable.]

Exercise 1.7b

1. Given that $X \sim Po(14)$ use Poisson tables to evaluate (a) $P(X = 15)$, (b) $P(X > 20)$, (c) $P(10 < X < 15)$. Use a normal distribution to find approximate values for these probabilities and comment on their accuracies.

2. The number of telephone calls per hour to a business office has a Poisson distribution with mean 48. Find approximate values for the probabilities that in one hour the number of calls will be (a) exactly 45, (b) between 40 and 50, both inclusive, (c) more than 60.

3. The number of accidents along a certain stretch of motorway has a Poisson distribution, the mean number of accidents per week being 1.8. Find an approximate value for the probability that in a year of 52 weeks the number of accidents along this stretch of motorway will be less than 100.

4.	In a certain city an average of 35 babies are born per day. (a) Find approximate values for the probabilities that the number of babies born in a day will be (i) 25 or fewer, (ii) 30 or more. (b) Find the expected number of days in a year when 30 or more babies will be born.

5.	The number of emissions per minute from a radioactive source has the Poisson distribution with mean 36. (a) Find approximate values for the probability that in a minute the number of emissions will be from 35 to 38, inclusive. (b) Find an approximate value for the probability that in a period of 5 minutes the number of emissions will be less than 160.

6.	The number of eggs laid in a season by a certain insect has the Poisson distribution with mean 200. Find approximate values for the probabilities that in a season the number of eggs laid will be (a) more than 160, (b) from 180 to 240, inclusive.

7.	An insurance company offers policies to householders to cover damage to the house, the house contents and motor cars. The number of claims arriving in a year on these three types of policies are independent random variables having Poisson distributions with means 20, 50 and 30, respectively. Find approximate values for the probabilities that in a year

(a)	the number of claims on houses will be 25 or more,

(b)	the combined number of claims on houses and contents will be less than 80,

(c)	the total number of claims on all three types of policy will be between 95 and 102, inclusive.

Miscellaneous Questions on Chapter 1

[An asterisk indicates a part added to the set question to cover percentiles]

1.	(1987) A soft-drinks machine is regulated so as to deliver an average of 200 ml per cup. The actual amount delivered per cup is a normally distributed random variable having mean 200 ml and standard deviation 8 ml.

(a)	Given that the maximum capacity of a cup is 210 ml, find the probability that a cup will overflow.

(b)	Find, to the nearest ml, what the maximum capacity of each cup should be for only 1% of the cups to overflow.	[5]

2.	(1987) The continuous random variable X has probability density function f given by	$f(x) = 3x^2$,	for $0 < x < 1$,
	$f(x) = 0$,	otherwise.

Find the mean and the variance of (i) X, (ii) X^{-1}.	[5]

3. (1987) The continuous random variable X has probability density function f where

$$f(x) = \frac{25}{12(x+1)^3} \ , \ \text{for } 0 \le x \le 4,$$

$$f(x) = 0 , \qquad \text{otherwise.}$$

(i) Evaluate E(X + 1). Hence, or otherwise, find the mean of X. [4]

(ii) Find the value of c > 0 for which P(X ≤ c) = c. [4]

(iii) *Find the median of X correct to three decimal places.

4. (1988) The length of each side of a cube is X cm, where X is a continuous random variable having probability density function f given by

$$f(x) = 2x^{-2} , \qquad \text{for } 1 \le x \le 2$$

$$f(x) = 0 , \qquad \text{otherwise.}$$

Find the mean and the variance of the volumes of the cubes. [5]

5. (1988) Suppose that the heights of adult males are normally distributed with mean 174.5 cm and standard deviation 10 cm.

(i) Calculate the probability that the height of a randomly chosen adult male will be greater than 175 cm. [2]

(ii) Use a distributional approximation to calculate the probability that at least 40 of 80 randomly chosen males will have heights greater than 175 cm. [4]

6. (1988) The continuous random variable X, which is restricted to values in the interval from 2 to 4, has cumulative distribution function F given by

$$F(x) = ax^2 + bx , \qquad \text{for } 2 \le x \le 4.$$

(i) Giving a clear indication of your method, show that $a = \frac{1}{8}$ and $b = -\frac{1}{4}$. [3]

(ii) Find the value of c such that P(X > c) = 0.88. [3]

(iii) Let N denote the integer obtained by rounding an observed value of X to its nearest integer value. Find the probability distribution of N and, hence, evaluate E(N).

[4]

(iv) *Find an expression for x_p, the $100p^{th}$ percentile of the distribution. Hence, or otherwise, calculate the median and the quartiles.

7. (1989) The random variable X is normally distributed with mean μ (> 0) and standard deviation 0.1 μ. (i) If μ = 5 find the probability that a randomly observed value of X will be greater than 5.5. (ii) Find the value of μ, correct to two decimal places, if the probability of a randomly observed value of X being greater than 30 is equal to 0.4. [5]

8. (1989) The continuous random variable X has probability density function f given by

$$f(x) = a(x - b) , \qquad \text{for } 2 \le x \le 5,$$

$$f(x) = 0 , \qquad \text{otherwise,}$$

where a and b are constants.

(i)   Given that a is positive write down the largest possible value that b may have.

(ii) By integrating f(x) over an appropriate interval show that 21a − 6ab = 2.

(iii) Given that the mean of the distribution is 3.8, find the values of a and b, and show that the variance of the distribution is equal to 0.66.   [9]

9.   (1990) The continuous random variable X is distributed with probability density function f, where

$$f(x) = 2(2 - x), \quad \text{for } 1 \le x \le 2,$$
$$f(x) = 0, \qquad\qquad \text{otherwise.}$$

(i)   Evaluate the mean of X.

(ii) Find the expected value of the area of the rectangle having adjacent sides of lengths X cm and (5 − 2X) cm.   [5]

(iii) *Calculate the median and the interquartile range of the distribution.

10. (1991) Independently for each seed of a particular variety of flower that is sown, the probability that the seed will germinate is 0.8. Use a normal approximation to find the probability that exactly 324 of 400 seeds will germinate.   [3]

11. (1991) The continuous random variable X is distributed with probability density function f given by

$$f(x) = 12x^2(1 - x), \qquad \text{for } 0 \le x \le 1,$$
$$f(x) = 0, \qquad\qquad\quad \text{otherwise.}$$

Evaluate the mean and the variance of X. Deduce the mean and the variance of Y = 6 −5X.   [6]

12. (1991) The continuous random variable X is distributed with probability density function f given by

$$f(x) = \frac{4}{(x + 2)^2}, \quad \text{for } 0 \le x \le 2,$$
$$f(x) = 0, \qquad\qquad \text{otherwise.}$$

(i)   Find the cumulative distribution, F, of X. Hence, or otherwise, evaluate the conditional probability $P\left(X \le \frac{2}{3} \middle| X > \frac{1}{3} \right)$.   [6]

(ii) Evaluate E(X + 2) and E[(X + 2)²]. Hence, or otherwise, find the mean and the variance of X.   [4]

13. (1992) Mass-produced pipes have internal diameters that are normally distributed with mean 10 cm and standard deviation 0.4 cm.

(i)   Calculate the probability that a randomly chosen pipe will have an internal diameter greater than 10.3 cm.

(ii) Find the value of d, correct to two decimal places, if 95% of the pipes have internal diameters greater than d cm.   [4]

14. (1992) The continuous random variable X has probability density function f given

by $\quad\quad\quad$ f(x) = 3c , $\quad\quad\quad$ for $0 \le x \le 1$,

$\quad\quad\quad\quad\quad$ f(x) = c(4 − x) , $\quad\quad$ for $1 \le x \le 4$,

$\quad\quad\quad\quad\quad$ f(x) = 0 , $\quad\quad\quad\quad$ otherwise.

(a) $\quad$ Show that c = 2/15. $\quad\quad\quad\quad\quad\quad\quad\quad\quad\quad\quad\quad\quad\quad$ [2]

(b) $\quad$ Find the mean value of X. $\quad\quad\quad\quad\quad\quad\quad\quad\quad\quad\quad\quad\quad$ [3]

(c) $\quad$ Find expressions for F(x), where F is the cumulative distribution function of X, indicating clearly the values of x for which each expression is valid. Hence, or otherwise, evaluate P(0.5 < X < 2.5). $\quad\quad\quad\quad\quad\quad\quad\quad\quad$ [6]

(d) $\quad$ *Calculate the median and the quartiles of the distribution.

15. (1993) The length of a certain mass-produced item is normally distributed with mean 24.3 cm and standard deviation 0.4 cm. An item is rejected if its length is less than 23.7 cm or greater than 25.2 cm. Calculate

(a) $\quad$ the percentage of items that are rejected,

(b) $\quad$ the percentage of the **rejected** items that are more than 25.2 cm long $\quad$ [5]

16. (1993) A motorist frequently travels from one town to another 132 km apart. The route taken by the motorist consists of 60 km of motorway and 72 km of non-motorway roads. The car's average speed on the motorway is 100 km per hour and on non-motorway roads is X km per hour, where X is a continuous random variable having probability density function f given by

$\quad\quad\quad\quad\quad$ f(x) = x/2250 , $\quad\quad$ for $60 \le x \le 90$,

$\quad\quad\quad\quad\quad$ f(x) = 0 , $\quad\quad\quad\quad$ otherwise.

(a) $\quad$ Find the cumulative distribution function of X. $\quad\quad\quad\quad\quad\quad$ [3]

(b) $\quad$ Show that the time, T hours, to complete such a journey is T = 0.6 + 72/X. Hence, or otherwise, find (i) the probability that a journey will take longer than 1 hour 36 minutes, (ii) the expected time to complete the journey. $\quad\quad\quad\quad$ [7]

17. (1994) The continuous random variable X has probability density function f, where

$\quad\quad\quad\quad\quad$ f(x) = kx(4 − x^2) , $\quad\quad\quad$ for $0 \le x \le 2$,

$\quad\quad\quad\quad\quad$ f(x) = 0 , $\quad\quad\quad\quad\quad\quad$ otherwise

(i) $\quad$ Show that k = 0.25. (ii) Calculate the mean value of X. $\quad\quad\quad\quad$ [5]

18. (1995) The random variable X has probability density function

$\quad\quad\quad\quad\quad$ f(x) = k(x − 1$)^2$, $\quad\quad\quad$ for $0 \le x \le 2$,

$\quad\quad\quad\quad\quad$ f(x) = 0 , $\quad\quad\quad\quad\quad\quad$ otherwise

(a) $\quad$ Find the value of the constant k.

(b) $\quad$ Find, for all values of x, the cumulative distribution function of X.

(c) $\quad$ Calculate P(0.5 < X < 1.5).

(d)   Find a such that P(X ≥ a) = 0.25.   [9]

(e)   *Calculate the 10-90 interpercentile range of the distribution.

19.   (S1 Jan 1996) You are given the exact ages of all of the pupils in your class and asked to round them down to an integer number of years, e.g. 17 years and 201 days becomes 17 years. If X days denotes the difference between the exact age and the rounded age (a) name a continuous distribution that could be used to model X, giving a reason for your choice, (b) use your model to write down the mean value of X.   [3]

20.   (S1 Jan 1996) The lengths of lizards of a certain species are normally distributed with mean 1.2 m and standard deviation 0.2 m.

(a)   Calculate the probability that the length of a randomly chosen lizard lies between 1.1 m and 1.6 m.   [3]

(b)   What length is exceeded by 2% of the lizards? Give your answer correct to two decimal places.   [3]

21.   (S1 Jan 1996) A PE teacher drives 12 miles to school along level roads by car. He finds, by observation over a year, that the journey time, T hours, can be modelled by a random variable with probability density function f given by

$$f(t) = k(t - 0.5) , \qquad \text{for } 0.5 \le t \le 1,$$
$$f(t) = 0 , \qquad \text{otherwise.}$$

(a)(i) Find the value of k.   [2]

(ii)   Calculate the mean journey time.   [3]

(iii)   Calculate the probability that T exceeds the mean.   [2]

(b)   The teacher now decides to run to the school. State with reasons, whether
(i) the mean, (ii) the standard deviation
of the journey time would now be smaller or larger than the corresponding values for the car journey.   [2]

(c)   *Calculate the median journey time correct to the nearest minute.

22.   (S1 June 1996) The marks awarded in a certain public examination are integers ranging from 0 to 100. Distinctions are awarded to candidates who obtain marks of 70 or more. The distribution of the marks obtained by the candidates is to be modelled by a normal distribution with mean 50 and standard deviation 13.

(a)   Use the model with a continuity correction to find, correct to one decimal place, the percentage of candidates obtaining distinctions.   [4]

(b)   Give one reason why the normal distribution does not provide a truly accurate model for the distribution of the marks obtained in the examination.   [1]

23. (S1 June 1996) The distribution of the annual summer rainfall, X cm, at a certain resort can be modelled by the probability density function f given by

$$f(x) = kx(9 - x^2) \qquad \text{for } 0 \le x \le 3$$
$$f(x) = 0 \qquad \text{otherwise}$$

where k is a constant.

(a) Show that the cumulative distribution function F of X is given, for $0 \le x \le 3$, by

$$F(x) = \frac{kx^2(18 - x^2)}{4}.$$ [2]

(i) Deduce that k = 4/81. [2]

(ii) Find the probability that X lies between 1 and 2. [2]

(b) Calculate E(X). [3]

24. (A3 1996) The wingspans of birds of a certain species are normally distributed with mean μ m and standard deviation σ m. Given that 4.4% of wingspans exceed 1.25 m, show that

$$\mu + 1.706\sigma = 1.25.$$ [2]

Given further that 3.4% of wingspans are less than 1.04 m,

(a) obtain a second equation involving μ and σ, [2]

(b) calculate μ and σ, each correct to three significant figures. [3]

25. (A3 1996) The distribution of the daily amount of petrol, X thousand litres, sold by a service station, is modelled by the probability density function f given by

$$f(x) = kx^2(4 - x), \qquad \text{for } 0 \le x \le 4,$$
$$f(x) = 0, \qquad \text{otherwise.}$$

(a) Show that k = 3/64. [2]

(b) Calculate the mean and the variance of X. [5]

(c) State one reason why the above model might not be accurate. [1]

Chapter 2

Two or More Random Variables

2.1   Two discrete random variables

Let X and Y denote two discrete random variables with either both associated with the outcomes of one random experiment, or one of the two is associated with the outcomes of one random experiment and the other is associated with the outcomes of another random experiment. Denote the possible values of X by $x_1, x_2, \ldots, x_r$ and the possible values of Y by $y_1, y_2, \ldots, y_s$. The joint distribution of X and Y will then be a specification of $P(X = x_i \cap Y = y_j)$ for every (x_i, y_j). We shall use p_{ij} to represent $P(X = x_i \cap Y = y_j)$. Note that the sum of all the p_{ij} will be equal to 1 and that some of them may be zero.

Since $X = x_i$ must occur with any one of the y_j, the distribution of X is

$$P(X = x_i) = p_{i1} + p_{i2} + \ldots + p_{is}, \text{ for } i = 1,2,3,\ldots, r \tag{1}$$

Similarly, the distribution of Y is

$$P(Y = y_j) = p_{1j} + p_{2j} + \ldots + p_{rj}, \text{ for } j = 1,2,3,\ldots, s \tag{2}$$

Definition: The **expected value** of any function h(X,Y) of X and Y is defined by

$$E[h(X,Y)] = \sum_{i=1}^{r} \sum_{j=1}^{s} h(x_i, y_j) p_{ij} \tag{3}$$

This is an extension of the definition given earlier of the expected value of a function of one random variable. Consider the particular function $h(X, Y) = aX + bY$, where a and b are constants. From (3)

$$E(aX + bY) = \sum_{i=1}^{r} \sum_{j=1}^{s} (ax_i + by_j) p_{ij}$$

$$= a\sum_{i=1}^{r} \sum_{j=1}^{s} x_i p_{ij} + b\sum_{i=1}^{r} \sum_{j=1}^{s} y_j p_{ij}$$

$$= a\sum_{i=1}^{r} x_i \left(\sum_{j=1}^{s} p_{ij}\right) + b\sum_{j=1}^{s} y_j \left(\sum_{i=1}^{r} p_{ij}\right)$$

$$= a\sum_{i=1}^{r} x_i P(X = x_i) + b\sum_{j=1}^{s} y_j P(Y = y_j)$$

on using (1) and (2) above. Hence

$$E(aX + bY) = aE(X) + bE(Y). \tag{4}$$

This is a very useful result as it enables us to find the expected value of aX + bY without first finding its distribution on knowing only the separate distributions of X and Y. The result can be generalised to

$$E[ag(X,Y) + bh(X,Y)] = aE[g(X,Y)] + bE[h(X,Y)] \qquad (5)$$

For example,

$$E(3X - 2Y) = 3E(X) - 2E(Y),$$

$$E(2X^2Y - 3X^3) = 2E(X^2Y) - 3E(X^3)$$

$$E[X(X - 2Y)] \equiv E(X^2 - 2XY) = E(X^2) - 2E(XY)$$

Example

Two balls are drawn at random without replacement from a box containing 2 red balls, 3 white balls and 5 blue balls. Let X denote the number of red balls drawn and let Y denote the number of white balls drawn.

(a)   Find the distributions of X and Y.

(b)   Find the distribution of the total score if each red ball drawn scores 4 points, each white ball drawn scores 2 points, and each blue ball drawn scores zero.

(c)   Use your results to verify that (4) above is true in this example.

Solution

(a) The possible values of X are 0, 1, 2, whose probabilities are

$$P(X = 0) = P(\text{no red ball}) = \binom{8}{2} / \binom{10}{2} = \frac{28}{45},$$

$$P(X = 1) = P(\text{1 red ball}) = \binom{2}{1} \times \binom{8}{1} / \binom{10}{2} = \frac{16}{45},$$

$$P(X = 2) = P(\text{2 red balls}) = \binom{2}{2} / \binom{10}{2} = \frac{1}{45}.$$

Thus, the distribution of X is as shown in the following table.

x	0	1	2
P(X = x)	$\frac{28}{45}$	$\frac{16}{45}$	$\frac{1}{45}$

Similarly, it may be shown that the distribution of Y is as follows.

y	0	1	2
P(Y = y)	$\frac{21}{45}$	$\frac{21}{45}$	$\frac{3}{45}$

(b) Since each red ball drawn scores 4 points, each white ball drawn scores 2 points, and each blue ball drawn scores nothing, the total score from the two balls drawn is

$$T = 4X + 2Y.$$

To find the distribution of T we need to determine its possible values and the probabilities of these values. This is most conveniently done by listing all the possible values of (X, Y), their probabilities and the corresponding values of T. This is done in the following table .

Number drawn			X	Y	Probability	T = 4X + 2Y
Red	White	Blue				
2	0	0	2	0	$\binom{2}{2} / \binom{10}{2} = \dfrac{1}{45}$	8
1	1	0	1	1	$\binom{2}{1} \times \binom{3}{1} / \binom{10}{2} = \dfrac{6}{45}$	6
1	0	1	1	0	$\binom{2}{1} \times \binom{5}{1} / \binom{10}{2} = \dfrac{10}{45}$	4
0	2	0	0	2	$\binom{3}{2} / \binom{10}{2} = \dfrac{3}{45}$	4
0	1	1	0	1	$\binom{3}{1} \times \binom{5}{1} / \binom{10}{2} = \dfrac{15}{45}$	2
0	0	2	0	0	$\binom{5}{2} / \binom{10}{2} = \dfrac{10}{45}$	0

Extracting appropriately from the table the distribution of T is:

t	0	2	4	6	8
P(T = t)	$\frac{10}{45}$	$\frac{15}{45}$	$\frac{13}{45}$	$\frac{6}{45}$	$\frac{1}{45}$

[Note that the probabilities add to 1 as required]

(c) From this table we find that

$$E(T) = 0 \times \tfrac{10}{45} + 2 \times \tfrac{15}{45} + 4 \times \tfrac{13}{45} + 6 \times \tfrac{6}{45} + 8 \times \tfrac{1}{45} = \tfrac{126}{45} .$$

From the distributions of X and Y obtained in (a) we find

$$E(X) = 0 \times \tfrac{28}{45} + 1 \times \tfrac{16}{45} + 2 \times \tfrac{1}{45} = \tfrac{18}{45}$$

and

$$E(Y) = 0 \times \tfrac{21}{45} + 1 \times \tfrac{21}{45} + 2 \times \tfrac{3}{45} = \tfrac{27}{45}$$

Substituting the values for E(X) and E(Y) in (4) we have

$$E(4X + 2Y) = 4E(X) + 2E(Y) = 4 \times \tfrac{18}{45} + 2 \times \tfrac{27}{45} = \tfrac{126}{45} = E(T),$$

which verifies the validity of (4) in this example.

Exercise 2.1

1. Given that $E(X) = 5$, $E(X^2) = 30$, $E(Y) = 2$, $Var(Y) = 4$, and $E(XY) = 3$, evaluate

   (a) $E(3X - 2Y)$, (b) $E(X^2 - 10Y)$, (c) $E[X(X - 5Y)]$, (d) $E[(X - Y)^2]$, (e) $Var(X - Y)$

2. Three numbers are drawn at random without replacement from the numbers 1,2,3,4,5.

(a) List all the possible combinations of the three numbers that are drawn.

(b) Let X denote the largest and Y the smallest of the three numbers drawn. Determine the distribution of $U = X - 2Y$ and evaluate $E(U)$.

(c) Derive the distributions of X and Y and hence the values of $E(X)$ and $E(Y)$. Use (4) above to deduce the value of $E(U)$ checking that your answer agrees with that obtained in (b) .

3. Two fair coins are tossed together. The coins showing heads are then tossed again. Let X denote the number of heads obtained on the first toss and let Y denote the number of heads on the second toss.

(a) Evaluate $E(X)$ and $E(Y)$.

(b) Find the distribution of $T = X - Y$ and deduce the value of $E(T)$.

(c) Use your results to verify the truth of (4).

4. A fair cubical die has four faces numbered 0 and each of the other two faces numbered 1. The die is thrown three times. Let X denote the sum of the three scores and let Y denote the number of times the score was 0.

(a) Evaluate $E(X)$ and $E(Y)$.

(b) Find the distribution of XY and show that $E(XY) \neq E(X)E(Y)$.

2.2 Two independent discrete random variables

Recall that two events A and B are independent if and only if
$$P(A \cap B) = P(A)P(B).$$
This prompts the following definition for two discrete random variables to be independent.

Definition: The discrete random variables X and Y are **independent** if and only if
$$P(X = x_i \cap Y = y_j) = P(X = x_i) \times P(Y = y_j) \text{ for all } (x_i, y_j)$$
A situation of particular interest is that where X and Y are associated with independent random experiments, in which case X and Y are clearly independent. For example, X may be the number of heads obtained in ten tosses of a coin and Y may be the sum of the scores when a die is thrown twice.

Example 1

Ann is to toss a fair coin twice and Brenda is to toss a fair coin three times. Find the probability that Ann will toss more heads than Brenda.

Solution

Let X denote the number of heads tossed by Ann and let Y denote the number of heads tossed by Brenda. Then, $X \sim B(2, \frac{1}{2})$ and, independently, $Y \sim B(3, \frac{1}{2})$. We need to find $P(X > Y)$. The event $\{X > Y\}$ will occur if any one of

$$\{(X = 2) \cap (Y = 0)\} \text{ or } \{(X = 2) \cap (Y = 1)\} \text{ or } \{(X = 1) \cap (Y = 0)\} \text{ occurs,}$$

the events in $\{\ \}$ being mutually exclusive. Since X and Y are independent,

$$P(X > Y) = P(X = 2)P(Y = 0) + P(X = 2)P(Y = 1) + P(X = 1)P(Y = 0)$$
$$= \frac{1}{4} \times \frac{1}{8} + \frac{1}{4} \times \frac{3}{8} + \frac{1}{2} \times \frac{1}{8} = \frac{6}{32} = \frac{3}{16}.$$

Example 2

X and Y are independent random variables having the distributions shown in the following tables:

x	2	3
P(X = x)	0.6	0.4

y	1	2	3	4
P(Y = y)	0.2	0.3	0.3	0.2

Find the distribution of $W = 2X - Y$ and determine its mean and variance.

Solution

The following table lists the possible pairs of values of X and Y, the corresponding values of W and their probabilities.

X	Y	W = 2X – Y	Probability
2	1	3	$0.6 \times 0.2 = 0.12$
2	2	2	$0.6 \times 0.3 = 0.18$
2	3	1	$0.6 \times 0.3 = 0.18$
2	4	0	$0.6 \times 0.2 = 0.12$
3	1	5	$0.4 \times 0.2 = 0.08$
3	2	4	$0.4 \times 0.3 = 0.12$
3	3	3	$0.4 \times 0.3 = 0.12$
3	4	2	$0.4 \times 0.2 = 0.08$

[Note that the probabilities do add to 1 as they should].

Extracting the possible values of W and their probabilities the distribution of W is as follows.

w	0	1	2	3	4	5
P(W = w)	0.12	0.18	0.26	0.24	0.12	0.08

$E(W) = 1 \times 0.18 + 2 \times 0.26 + 3 \times 0.24 + 4 \times 0.12 + 5 \times 0.08 = 2.3.$

$E(W^2) = 1 \times 0.18 + 4 \times 0.26 + 9 \times 0.24 + 16 \times 0.12 + 25 \times 0.08 = 7.3.$

$Var(W) = 7.3 - 2.3^2 = 2.01.$

Exercise 2.2a

1. A fair cubical die is tossed twice. Calculate the probability that the score obtained on the second throw is at least twice the score obtained on the first throw.

2. Given that $X \sim B(5, 0.4)$ and, independently, $Y \sim Po(2)$ evaluate (a) $P(X > 2Y)$, (b) $P(XY = 0)$, giving your answers correct to three decimal places.

3. Let X denote the number of heads obtained in 3 tosses of a fair coin and let Y denote the number of 6's obtained in 2 throws of a fair die. Evaluate $P(X + Y \leq 2)$.

4. X and Y are independent random variables with X having the binomial distribution $B(3, \frac{1}{2})$ and Y the Poisson distribution Po(2). Find, in terms of e, the probability that   (a)   each of X and Y will have the value zero,

      (b) X and Y will have the same value.

5. Two balls are drawn at random *with replacement* from box A which contains 5 red balls and 4 blue balls. At the same time three balls are drawn at random *with replacement* from box B which contains 5 red balls and 5 blue balls. Calculate the probability that (a) the combined number of red balls drawn is equal to 4, (b) the number of red balls drawn from box A is greater than the number of red balls drawn from box B.

6. With X and Y as defined in Example 2 above find the distribution of $S = X + Y$ and calculate its mean and variance.

Additive property of two independent Poisson random variables

If X and Y are independent with $X \sim Po(\alpha)$ and $Y \sim Po(\beta)$ then

$$X + Y \sim Po(\alpha + \beta).$$

Proof

Let $S = X + Y$. The possible values of S are s = 0, 1, 2, 3, ... We need to find an expression for $P(S = s)$ and show that it is consistent with S having the distribution $Po(\alpha + \beta)$.

The event {S = s} occurs only if X and Y take the values

$\{(X = 0) \cap (Y = s)\}$ or $\{(X = 1) \cap (Y = s - 1)\}$ or . . . or $\{(X = s) \cap (Y = 0)\}$.

Since the events in $\{\ \}$ are mutually exclusive and X and Y are independent

$$P(S = s) = P(X = 0)P(Y = s) + P(X = 1)P(Y = s - 1) + \cdots + P(X = s)P(Y = 0)\}$$

That is, $P(S = s)$ is the sum of $P(X = x)P(Y = s - x)$ for $x = 0, 1, 2, \ldots, s$.

Now,

$$P(X = x)P(Y = s - x) = \left(e^{-\alpha} \times \frac{\alpha^x}{x!} \right) \times \left(e^{-\beta} \times \frac{\beta^{s-x}}{(s-x)!} \right)$$

$$= \frac{e^{-(\alpha+\beta)} \alpha^x \beta^{s-x}}{x!(s-x)!}$$

$$= e^{-(\alpha+\beta)} \binom{s}{x} \frac{\alpha^x \beta^{s-x}}{s!}.$$

Hence,

$$P(S = s) = \frac{e^{-(\alpha+\beta)}}{s!} \left\{ \beta^s + \binom{s}{1} \alpha \beta^{s-1} + \binom{s}{2} \alpha^2 \beta^{s-2} + \cdots + \alpha^s \right\}$$

$$= \frac{e^{-(\alpha+\beta)}}{s!} (\beta + \alpha)^s, \quad \text{for } s = 0, 1, 2, 3, \ldots .$$

which we can identify as being $Po(\alpha + \beta)$.

Example 3

The numbers X, Y of outgoing and incoming calls at a telephone exchange during a lunch hour are independent random variables with X~Po(3) and Y~Po(5). (a) Calculate the probability that during a lunch hour the combined number of outgoing and incoming calls will be 3. (b) Given that there were 3 calls during a lunch hour calculate the probability that only one of them was an outgoing call.

Solution

(a)   Let $T = X + Y$ denote the combined number of outgoing and incoming calls during a lunch hour. By the additive property for independent Poisson distributions we know that $T \sim Po(3 + 5 = 8)$. Hence

$$P(T = 3) = e^{-8} \times \frac{8^3}{3!} = \frac{256e^{-8}}{3} \approx 0.0286.$$

(b)   We now need to evaluate $P(X = 1 | T = 3)$.

$$P(X = 1 | T = 3) = \frac{P(X = 1 \cap Y = 2)}{P(T = 3)}.$$

Since X and Y are independent the numerator is equal to

$$P(X = 1)P(Y = 2) = \left(e^{-3} \times 3\right) \times \left(e^{-5} \times \frac{5^2}{2!}\right) = \frac{75}{2}e^{-8}.$$

Using our result in (a)

$$P(X = 1|T = 3) = \frac{75}{2}e^{-8} \bigg/ \frac{256}{3}e^{-8} = \frac{225}{512} \approx 0.4395.$$

Exercise 2.2b

1. The numbers, X and Y, of emissions per minute from two independent radioactive sources have Poisson distributions with means 3.4 and 5.6, respectively. Calculate the probability that there will be fewer than 4 emissions in a minute from the two sources combined.

2. A shopkeeper has two shops which are supplied from a central store. The numbers of a particular product that the shops receive in a week have Poisson distributions with means 6 and 8, respectively. Find, correct to three decimal places, the probability that in a week the combined number of the product received by the two shops will be fewer than 12.

3. The number of times that my dishwasher will break down in a year has a Poisson distribution with mean 2.4, while the number of times that my washing machine will break down in a year has a Poisson distribution with mean 1.6. Calculate the probability that in a year (a) neither the dishwasher nor the washing machine will break down, (b) the total number of breakdowns will be less than 5.

4. In a cafeteria the numbers of cups of coffee and tea sold per minute may be assumed to be independent random variables having Poisson distributions with means 3 and 2, respectively. (a) Calculate the probability that in a minute the combined number of cups of coffee and tea sold is at least 4. (b) Given that the combined number sold in a minute was 4, calculate the probability that two cups of each beverage were sold.

5. The numbers X and Y of two types of bacterial organisms that may be present in a sample of liquid are independent random variables each having the Poisson distribution with mean μ. (a) Given that a sample of the liquid contained a total of 4 organisms, calculate the probability that there were 2 organisms of each type.

(b) Given that a sample contained at least one organism, show that the probability that all the organisms in the sample are of one type only is $2/(1 + e^\mu)$.

Some important properties of two independent discrete random variables

Let X and Y denote two independent random variables with X having the possible values $x_1, x_2, \ldots, x_r$ and Y the possible values $y_1, y_2, \ldots, y_s$.

Since X and Y are independent, their joint distribution is
$$P(X = x_i \cap Y = y_j) = P(X = x_i)P(Y = y_j) \text{ for } i = 1, 2, \cdots, r; \; j = 1, 2, \cdots, s.$$

Property 1

For any two functions g(X) and h(Y)
$$E[g(X)h(Y)] = E[g(X)]E[h(Y)]$$

From the definition of the expected value of any function of X and Y

$$
\begin{aligned}
E[g(X)h(Y)] &= \sum_{i=1}^{r}\sum_{j=1}^{s} g(x_i)h(y_j)P(X = x_i)P(Y = y_j) \\
&= \left\{\sum_{i=1}^{r} g(x_i)P(X = x_i)\right\} \times \left\{\sum_{j=1}^{s} h(y_j)P(Y = y_j)\right\} \\
&= E[g(X)]E[h(Y)].
\end{aligned}
$$

In particular, $E(XY) = E(X)E(Y)$.

Another example of the above property is $E(X^3Y^2) = E(X^3)E(Y^2)$.

Note that for independent X and Y, $E\left(\dfrac{X}{Y}\right) = E(X) \times E\left(\dfrac{1}{Y}\right)$ NOT $\dfrac{E(X)}{E(Y)}$.

Example 4

X and Y are random variables with $X \sim B(10, 0.6)$ and $Y \sim Po(4.5)$.

Find the mean and the variance of $W = XY$.

Solution

Since X and Y are independent, we have from Property 1 that
$$E(W) = E(XY) = E(X)E(Y) = 6 \times 4.5 = 27.$$
$$Var(W) = E(W^2) - [E(W)]^2 = E(X^2Y^2) - 27^2$$
$$= E(X^2)\,E(Y^2) - 27^2.$$

Now $E(X^2) = Var(X) + [E(X)]^2 = 10 \times 0.6 \times 0.4 + (10 \times 0.6)^2 = 38.4$,

and $E(Y^2) = Var(Y) + [E(Y)]^2 = 4.5 + (4.5)^2 = 24.75$.

Hence,
$$Var(W) = 38.4 \times 24.75 - 27^2 = 221.4.$$

[Note that the possible alternative method based on first finding the distribution of W is not possible here.]

Exercise 2.2c

1. X and Y are independent and such that $E(X) = 3$, $Var(X) = 1$, $E(Y) = 1$ and $Var(Y) = 4$. Evaluate (a) $E[X(X - Y)]$, (b) $Var(XY)$.

2. X and Y are independent and have the distributions shown in the following tables.

x	1	2	3	4
P(X = x)	0.1	0.3	0.5	0.1

y	1	2
P(Y = y)	0.6	0.4

    (a) Find the distributions of $U = \dfrac{1}{Y}$ and $W = \dfrac{X}{Y}$. Verify that $E\left(\dfrac{X}{Y}\right) = E(X) \times E\left(\dfrac{1}{Y}\right)$ and that their common value is not equal to $\dfrac{E(X)}{E(Y)}$. (b) Evaluate $E\left(\dfrac{X^2}{Y}\right)$.

3. X and Y are independent with X having the Poisson distribution Po(2) and Y the Poisson distribution Po(3). Find the mean and the standard deviation of $U = XY$.

4. The length of each side, X cm, of a square base of a cuboid is a random variable having the distribution shown in the following table.

x	5	10	15
P(X = x)	0.4	0.4	0.2

    Independently, the height, Y cm, of the cuboid is a random variable having the following distribution.

y	20	25	30
P(Y = y)	0.5	0.4	0.1

    Calculate the expected value of the volume of the cuboid.

5. A person draws a card at random from a pack of five cards numbered from 1 to 5, respectively, and then draws a card at random from another pack which consists of four cards numbered from 1 to 4, respectively. Find the mean and the variance of the product of the two numbers on the drawn cards.

Property 2

In Section 2.1 we showed that for any two random variables X and Y and for any two constants a and b,

$$E(aX + bY) = aE(X) + bE(Y).$$

We now show that if X and Y are independent then

$$Var(aX + bY) = a^2 Var(X) + b^2 Var(Y).$$

Proof

Let $Z = aX + bY$. Then, from the first of the above results

$$\mu_Z \equiv E(Z) = aE(X) + bE(Y) \equiv a\mu_X + b\mu_Y.$$

Thus,

$$Z - \mu_Z = a(X - \mu_X) + b(Y - \mu_Y)$$

and, therefore,

$$
\begin{aligned}
Var(Z) &\equiv E[(Z-\mu_Z)^2] \\
&= E[a^2(X - \mu_X)^2] + E[2ab(X - \mu_X)(Y - \mu_Y)] + E[b^2(Y - \mu_Y)^2] \\
&= a^2 Var(X) + b^2 Var(Y) + 2abE[(X - \mu_X)(Y - \mu_Y)].
\end{aligned}
$$

Since X and Y are independent

$$E[(X - \mu_X)(Y - \mu_Y)] = E(X - \mu_X)E(Y - \mu_Y) = 0.$$

Hence

$$Var(aX + bY) = a^2 Var(X) + b^2 Var(Y).$$

In particular, for independent X and Y

$$Var(X \pm Y) = Var(X) + Var(Y),$$

$$Var(2X - 3Y) = 4Var(X) + 9Var(Y).$$

Let us verify the above results for $E(aX + bY)$ and $Var(aX + bY)$ in the particular case given in Example 2 above. In that example X and Y were independent with the following distributions.

x	2	3
P(X = x)	0.6	0.4

y	1	2	3	4
P(Y = y)	0.2	0.3	0.3	0.2

We showed that $E(2X - Y) = 2.3$ and $Var(2X - Y) = 2.01$.

Now compare these with $2E(X) - E(Y)$ and $4Var(X) + Var(Y)$, respectively.

$$E(X) \ = \ 2 \times 0.6 + 3 \times 0.4 \ = \ 2.4,$$
$$E(Y) \ = \ 1 \times 0.2 + 2 \times 0.3 + 3 \times 0.3 + 4 \times 0.2 \ = \ 2.5.$$

Hence, $2E(X) - E(Y) = 2 \times 2.4 - 2.5 = 2.3$, as obtained earlier.

$$E(X^2) \ = \ 4 \times 0.6 + 9 \times 0.4 \ = \ 6.0,$$

$$Var(X) \ = \ 6.0 - 2.4^2 \ = \ 0.24.$$

$$E(Y^2) \ = \ 1 \times 0.2 + 4 \times 0.3 + 9 \times 0.3 + 16 \times 0.2 \ = \ 7.3,$$

$$Var(Y) \ = \ 7.3 - 2.5^2 \ = \ 1.05$$

Thus,

$4\,Var(X) + Var(Y) = 4 \times 0.24 + 1.05 = 2.01$, as obtained earlier.

Example 5

X and Y are independent with $X \sim B(50, 0.2)$ and $Y \sim Po(10)$. Find the mean and the variance of (a) $Y - X$, (b) $2X + 3Y$, (c) $Y - \frac{1}{2}X$.

Solution

Since $X \sim B(50, 0.2)$, $E(X) = 50 \times 0.2 = 10$, $Var(X) = 50 \times 0.2 \times 0.8 = 8$.

Since $Y \sim Po(10)$, $E(Y) = Var(Y) = 10$.

(a) $E(Y - X) = E(Y) - E(X) = 10 - 10 = 0.$

Since X and Y are independent, $Var(Y - X) = Var(Y) + Var(X) = 8 + 10 = 18.$

(b) $E(2X + 3Y) = 2E(X) + 3E(Y) = 2 \times 10 + 3 \times 10 = 50.$

  $Var(2X + 3Y) = 4\,Var(X) + 9\,Var(Y) = 4 \times 8 + 9 \times 10 = 122.$

(c) $E(Y - \frac{1}{2}X) = E(Y) - \frac{1}{2}E(X) = 10 - \frac{1}{2} \times 10 = 5.$

  $Var(Y - \frac{1}{2}X) = Var(Y) + \frac{1}{4}Var(X) = 10 + \frac{1}{4} \times 8 = 12.$

Exercise 2.2d

1. Given that X and Y are independent with $X \sim B(20, 0.6)$ and $Y \sim B(10, 0.3)$, find the mean and the variance of (a) $X - Y$, (b) $X - 4Y$, (c) $\frac{1}{4}X - \frac{1}{2}Y$.

2. A fair die is thrown twice. Let X denote the score on the first throw and let Y denote the score on the second throw. Random variables U and W are defined by $U = X + Y$ and $W = 3X - 2Y$. Evaluate (a) E(U), (b) Var(U), (c) Var(W), (d) E(UW).

3. X and Y are independent with X ~ Po(5) and Y ~ Po(8). Find the mean and the variance of (a) X + Y, (b) 2Y – 3X, (c) Y – X. Give one reason why the distribution of Y – X cannot be Poisson.

4. Two types of flaws, A and B, may occur in manufactured cloth. The numbers of flaws of type A and type B occurring per metre length of the cloth are independent random variables having Poisson distributions with means 0.5 and 1, respectively. Removing a type A flaw from the cloth costs 8 pence and removing a type B flaw costs 2 pence. Find the mean and the standard deviation of the cost of removing flaws per metre length of the cloth.

5. During its first year the number of times that a new car has to be returned to the dealer for attention has the Poisson distribution with mean 0.5. Independently, during its second year the number of times that the car has to be returned to the dealer for attention has the Poisson distribution with mean 1.4.

(a) Write down the mean and the variance of the total number of times in its first two years that the car has to be returned to the dealer for attention.

Suppose that during its third year the number of times that the car has to be returned to the dealer for attention is exactly twice the number of times it had to be returned in its second year.

(b) Find the mean and the variance of the total number of times in its first three years that the car has to be returned to the dealer for attention.

2.3 Three or more independent discrete random variables

The results obtained above for two independent random variables extend in an obvious way to three or more independent random variables. The extensions to three independent random variables X, Y and Z are as follows.

(1) If X, Y and Z are independent with X ~ Po(α), Y ~ Po(β), and Z ~ Po(γ) then
$$X + Y + Z ~ Po(\alpha + \beta + \gamma).$$

(2) For *any* three random variables X, Y and Z and constants a, b and c,
$$E(aX + bY + cZ) = aE(X) + bE(Y) + cE(Z).$$

(3) If X, Y and Z are independent then
   (a) $E[f(X)g(Y)h(Z)] = E[f(X)] \times E[g(Y)] \times E[h(Z)]$,

so that, in particular, $E(XYZ) = E(X) \times E(Y) \times E(Z)$;
   (b) $Var(aX + bY + cZ) = a^2 Var(X) + b^2 Var(Y) + c^2 Var(Z)$,

for any constants a, b and c.

The results stated in (2) and 3(b) provide us with an alternative method for deriving the mean and variance of B(n, p) which is much simpler than the method used in the S1 book.

Consider a random experiment in each trial of which the probability of a success is p. If X is the number of successes in n independent trials then we know that X ~ B(n, p).

Now introduce n random variables $X_1, X_2, \ldots, X_n$, where X_r is associated with the outcome of the rth trial (r = 1, 2, ... , n) and defined by

$$X_r = 1 \text{ if the } r^{th} \text{ trial is a success,}$$
$$X_r = 0 \text{ otherwise.}$$

Observe that $X_1 + X_2 + \ldots + X_n = X$, the number of successes in the n trials. Using (2) above we have

$$E(X) = E(X_1) + E(X_2) + \ldots + E(X_n).$$

Also, since the trials are independent, so are $X_1, X_2, \ldots, X_n$ independent so that by (3)(b) above

$$Var(X) = Var(X_1) + Var(X_2) + \ldots + Var(X_n).$$

Each X_r has the distribution
$$P(X_r = 1) = p \text{ and } P(X_r = 0) = 1 - p.$$

Thus, for r = 1, 2, ... , n
$$E(X_r) = 1 \times p + 0 \times (1 - p) = p.$$
$$E(X_r^2) = 1^2 \times p + 0^2 \times (1 - p) = p$$

so that $\quad Var(X_r) = p - p^2 = p(1 - p).$

Hence, $\quad E(X) = np$ and $Var(X) = np(1 - p).$

Exercise 2.3

1. The numbers of men, women and children arriving per hour at a doctor's surgery are independent random variables having Poisson distributions with means 4, 3 and 2, respectively. Find, correct to three decimal places, the probability that in an hour (a) at least 3 adults will arrive, (b) no more than 3 patients will arrive.

2. An insurance company offers policies covering houses, the contents of houses, and cars. The numbers of claims received per day on these policies may be assumed to have Poisson distributions with means 2, 3 and 5, respectively. Find the probability that in a day the company will receive more than 12 claims in total.

3. A county has four fire stations. The number of false calls per day to each station has the Poisson distribution with mean 1.5. Assuming that false calls to the stations are independent, find the probability that in a day the total number of false calls to the four stations will be exactly 6.

4. X, Y and Z are independent random variables such that
    $E(X) = 2$, $Var(X) = 4$, $E(Y) = 3$, $Var(Y) = 1$, $E(Z) = 4$, $Var(Z) = 9$.
    Find the mean and the variance of (a) X + Y + Z, (b) 2X − 3Y + Z, (c) XYZ.

5. The lengths of the sides of a cuboid are independent random variables each having the following distribution.

x	5	10	15
P(X = x)	0.6	0.2	0.2

    Find the mean and the variance of the volume of such a cuboid.

2.4 Two or more continuous random variables

The following definition for two continuous random variables to be independent is an adaptation of that given in Section 2.2 for two discrete random variables.

Definition: The continuous random variables X and Y are independent if and only if
$$P[(a \leq X \leq b) \cap (c \leq Y \leq d)] = P(a \leq X \leq b) \times P(c \leq Y \leq d) \qquad (1)$$
for all constants a, b, c and d.

The properties of expected value and variance given in Sections 2.1 and 2.2 are equally valid for continuous random variables. These properties are:

For any two continuous random variables X and Y,
$$E[c_1 h_1(X) + c_2 h_2(Y)] = c_1 E[h_1(X)] + c_2 E[h_2(Y)] \qquad (2a)$$
and, in particular,
$$E(aX \pm bY) = aE(X) \pm bE(Y) \qquad (2b)$$
If X and Y are independent then
$$E[h_1(X)h_2(Y)] = E[h_1(X)] \times E[h_2(Y)] \qquad (3a)$$
and, in particular,
$$E(XY) = E(X) \times E(Y). \qquad (3b)$$
$$Var(aX \pm bY) = a^2 Var(X) + b^2 Var(Y) \qquad (4)$$

As mentioned in Section 2.3 the above results extend in an obvious manner to three or more random variables. In particular,

(1) If X, Y and Z are three random variables and a, b and c are constants

$$E(aX + bY + cZ) = aE(X) + bE(Y) + cE(Z).$$

(2) If X, Y and Z are independent random variables then

(a) $\quad E[f(X)g(Y)h(Z)] = E[f(X)] \times E[g(Y)] \times E[h(Z)],$

so that, in particular ,

$$E(XYZ) = E(X) \times E(Y) \times E(Z).$$

(b) $Var(aX + bY + cZ) = a^2Var(X) + b^2Var(Y) + c^2Var(Z)$

Example 1

X and Y are independent with X having the uniform distribution U(10, 20), and Y having the normal distribution N(15, 4^2). Evaluate (a) $P[(X \le 16) \cap (Y \le 16)]$, (b) $E(3X - Y)$,

(c) $Var(3X - Y)$, (d) $E(Y^2/X^3)$.

Solution

(a) Since X and Y are independent

$$P[(X \le 16) \cap (Y \le 16)] \;=\; P(X \le 16) \times P(Y \le 16)$$

Since $X \sim U(10, 20)$ $\quad P(X \le 16) \;=\; \dfrac{16 - 10}{20 - 10} \;=\; 0.6.$

Since $Y \sim N(15, 4^2)$ $\quad P(Y \le 16) \;=\; P\!\left(Z \le \dfrac{16 - 15}{4}\right) \;=\; P(Z \le 0.25) \;=\; 0.59871.$

Hence $\quad P[(X \le 16) \cap (Y \le 16)] \;=\; 0.6 \times 0.59871 \;=\; 0.359$ to 3 decimal places.

(b) Using (2b) above $\quad E(3X - Y) = 3E(X) - E(Y) \;=\; 3(10 + 20)/2 - 15 \;=\; 30.$

(c) Using (4) above $\quad Var(3X - Y) = 9Var(X) + Var(Y)$

Since $X \sim U(10, 20)$, $\quad Var(X) \;=\; (20 - 10)^2/12 \;=\; 100/12 \;=\; 25/3.$

Hence $\quad Var(3X - Y) \;=\; 9 \times (25/3) + 16 \;=\; 91.$

(d) Using (3a) above $\quad E(Y^2/X^3) \;=\; E(Y^2 \times 1/X^3) \;=\; E(Y^2) \times E(1/X^3).$

The probability density function of X is

$$f(x) = \dfrac{1}{10} , \quad \text{for } 10 \le x \le 20$$

Hence $\quad E\!\left(\dfrac{1}{X^3}\right) \;=\; \dfrac{1}{10} \int_{10}^{20} \dfrac{1}{x^3}\, dx \;=\; \dfrac{1}{20}\left[-\dfrac{1}{x^2}\right]_{10}^{20} \;=\; 0.000375.$

$$E(Y^2) \;=\; Var(Y) + [E(Y)]^2 \;=\; 16 + 15^2 \;=\; 241.$$

Thus, $\quad E(Y^2/X^3) \;=\; 0.000375 \times 241 \;=\; 0.090375.$

Example 2

A manufacturer produces rods of two types, A and B. Rods of type A have lengths in cm that are uniformly distributed over the interval (10,15), while rods of type B have lengths in cm that are normally distributed with mean 12 and standard deviation 1. If one rod of each type is chosen at random (a) calculate the probability that the longer of the two chosen rods will be more than 13 cm long, (b) find the mean and the variance of the amount by which the length of the type A rod exceeds the length of the type B rod.

Solution

Let X cm denote the length of the chosen type A rod, and let Y cm denote the length of the chosen type B rod. It is clear that X and Y are independent. We are given that $X \sim U(10, 15)$ and $Y \sim N(12,1)$.

(a) Let W cm denote the length of the longer of the two rods. We need to evaluate $P(W > 13)$. The event $(W > 13)$ will occur only if at least one of X and Y is greater than 13, the complement of which is that neither X nor Y is greater than 13, or equivalently that each of X and Y is less than or equal to 13. Hence

$$P(W > 13) \; = \; 1 - P(W \le 13) = 1 - P(X \le 13) \times P(Y \le 13)$$

$$P(X \le 13) \; = \; \frac{13 - 10}{15 - 10} \; = \; 0.6,$$

$$P(Y \le 13) \; = \; P\left(Z \le \frac{13 - 12}{1}\right) \; = \; P(Z \le 1) \; = \; 0.84134$$

Thus, $\qquad P(W > 13) \; = \; 1 - 0.6 \times 0.84134 \; = \; 0.495$ to 3 decimal places.

(b) The amount in cm that the length of the rod of type A exceeds the length of the rod of type B is $X - Y$. Using (2b) and (4) above we have

$$E(X - Y) \; = \; E(X) - E(Y) \; = \; \frac{1}{2}(10 + 15) - 12 \; = \; 0.5$$

and $\qquad Var(X - Y) \; = \; Var(X) + Var(Y) \; = \; \frac{(15 - 10)^2}{12} + 1^2$

$$= \; 3.083 \text{ to 3 decimal places.}$$

Exercise 2.4a

1. If X and Y are independent random variables with $X \sim N(4, 1)$ and $Y \sim N(5, 4)$, find (a) $P[(X \le 3) \cap (Y > 3)]$, (b) the mean and variance of $3X - 2Y$.

2. X and Y are independent random variables having probability density functions f and g, where $\quad f(x) \quad = \; 3x^2, \qquad$ for $0 < x < 1,$
    $$g(y) \quad = \; 2(1 - y), \qquad \text{for } 0 < y < 1.$$

(a)   Find the probability that the smaller of a randomly observed value of X and a randomly observed value of Y will be less than $\frac{1}{2}$.

(b)   Find the probability that the larger of a randomly observed value of X and a randomly observed value of Y will be greater than $\frac{1}{2}$.

3.   Cuboids having square bases are such that the length in cm of a side of the base is uniformly distributed over the interval (2, 8), and independently, their heights in cm are uniformly distributed over the interval (4, 10). Find the mean and the variance of the volumes of the cuboids.

4.   X and Y are independent random variables with $X \sim U(0, 2)$ and $Y \sim U(1, 5)$. A rectangle is constructed with its adjacent sides having lengths X and Y, respectively. Find the mean and the variance of the area of the rectangle.

5.   The current, W amperes, that will flow through a circuit when the voltage across the circuit is X volts and the resistance in the circuit is Y ohms is given by $W = X/Y$. Suppose that X and Y are independent random variables having probability density functions f and g, where $f(x) = 6x(1 - x)$, for $0 \le x \le 1$, and $g(y) = 3y^2$, for $0 \le y \le 1$.

Find the mean and the variance of the current W through the circuit.

6.   Each of the longer sides of a rectangle has length X cm where $X \sim U(5, 9)$, and each of the shorter sides has length Y cm, where $Y \sim U(0, 1)$. Given that X and Y are independent find the mean and the variance of the perimeter of the rectangle.

7.   Manufactured rods have lengths that are distributed with mean 10 cm and standard deviation 0.5 cm. Find the mean and the variance of the combined length of (a) two randomly chosen rods,   (b) three randomly chosen rods.

8.   The number X of air bubbles in a mass produced lens is a discrete random variable such that

$$P(X = r) = \frac{1}{3} - \frac{r}{15}, \qquad r = 0, 1, 2, 3, 4.$$

A lens having two or more air bubbles is rejected as unsuitable. A lens having one or no air bubble is tested to determine its dispersion index. Such a lens is passed only if it has **either** no air bubble and a dispersion index less than 4, **or** one air bubble and a dispersion index less than 3.4. Independently of the number of air bubbles, the dispersion index of a lens is normally distributed with mean 3.6 and standard deviation 0.5.

(a)   Find the proportion of all lenses that will be passed, giving your answer correct to three decimal places.

(b)　One of the lenses that has been passed is chosen at random. Find, correct to three decimal places, the probability that the lens has no air bubble.

9.　The random variables X, Y and W are independent, with X having the binomial distribution B(10, 0.2), Y the uniform distribution U(5, 11), and W the normal distribution N(3.5, 0.5). Find the mean and the variance of $T = 2YW - 5X$.

Linear Combination of Independent Normal Random Variables

An important property of the normal distribution is that any linear combination of independent normally distributed random variables is also normally distributed.

Thus, if X and Y are independent and normally distributed, then for any constants a and b,

$$T = aX + bY$$

is also normally distributed with mean and variance given by

$$E(T) = aE(X) + bE(Y) \quad \text{and} \quad Var(T) = a^2 Var(X) + b^2 Var(Y).$$

In general, if $X_1, X_2, \ldots, X_n$ are independent with $X_i \sim N(\mu_i, \sigma_i^2)$, then for any constants $c_1, c_2, \ldots, c_n$,

$$T = c_1 X_1 + c_2 X_2 + \ldots + c_n X_n$$

is also normally distributed with mean and variance given by

$$E(T) = c_1 \mu_1 + c_2 \mu_2 + \ldots + c_n \mu_n,$$
$$Var(T) = c_1^2 \sigma_1^2 + c_2^2 \sigma_2^2 + \ldots + c_n^2 \sigma_n^2.$$

For example, if X_1, X_2, and X_3 are independent and normally distributed, then

$$T = 3X_1 - 2X_2 + X_3$$

is normally distributed with mean and variance given by

$$E(T) = 3E(X_1) - 2E(X_2) + E(X_3)$$
$$Var(T) = 9Var(X_1) + 4Var(X_2) + Var(X_3).$$

Example 3

The weights of male and female students at a large college may be assumed to be normally distributed, the males' weights having mean 69 kg and standard deviation 10 kg, and the females' weights having mean 56 kg and standard deviation 8 kg. (a) If one male and one female are chosen at random, calculate the probabilities that (i) the female is heavier than the male, (ii) the female's weight is at least $\frac{3}{4}$ of the male's weight. (b) If two males and one female are chosen at random, calculate the probability that the sum of their weights exceeds 200 kg.

Solution

Let X kg denote the weight of a randomly chosen male so that $X \sim N(69, 10^2)$, and let Y kg denote the weight of a randomly chosen female so that $Y \sim N(56, 8^2)$.

(a)(i) The female is heavier than the male if $Y > X$, that is if $Y - X > 0$.

Now $Y - X$ is normally distributed with mean

$$E(Y) - E(X) = 56 - 69 = -13$$

and variance $\quad Var(Y) + Var(X) = 64 + 100 = 164.$

$$P(Y - X > 0) = P\left(Z > \frac{0 - (-13)}{\sqrt{164}}\right) \approx P(Z > 1.02) = 0.154 \text{ to 3 decimal places.}$$

(ii) The female's weight is at least $\frac{3}{4}$ of the male's weight if $Y \geq \frac{3}{4}X$, or $4Y - 3X \geq 0$.

$4Y - 3X$ is normally distributed with mean

$$4E(Y) - 3E(X) = 4 \times 56 - 3 \times 69 = 17$$

and variance $\quad 16\,Var(Y) + 9\,Var(X) \quad = 16 \times 64 + 9 \times 100 = 1924.$

Therefore, $\qquad P(4Y - 3X \geq 0) = P\left(Z \geq \frac{0 - 17}{\sqrt{1924}}\right) \approx P(Z > -0.39)$

$$= P(Z < 0.39) = 0.652 \text{ to 3 decimal places.}$$

(b) Let X_1 and X_2 denote the weights of the two chosen males and let Y denote the weight of the chosen female. Note that X_1 and X_2 have the same distribution as X and that X_1, X_2 and Y are independent.

The sum of the weights of all three is $S = X_1 + X_2 + Y$, where S is normally distributed with mean $\qquad E(S) = E(X_1) + E(X_2) + E(Y) = 69 + 69 + 56 = 194$

and variance $\quad Var(S) = Var(X_1) + Var(X_2) + Var(Y) = 100 + 100 + 64 = 264.$

$$P(S > 200) = P\left(Z > \frac{200 - 194}{\sqrt{264}}\right) \approx P(Z > 0.37) = 0.356 \text{ to 3 decimal places.}$$

[Note: A fairly common error that may be made in answering (b) is to take $S = 2X + Y$, which assumes that each of the chosen males has the same weight X kg. Whereas this version of S will give the correct value for E(S) it will give an incorrect value for Var(S). The weights of the two chosen males are two independent observations of X.]

Example 4

A piece of equipment has to be assembled in three stages. The time W minutes taken to complete the first stage is normally distributed with mean 15.4 and standard deviation 3; the time X minutes taken to complete the second stage is normally distributed with mean 25.8 and standard deviation 4; and the time Y minutes taken to complete the third stage is normally distributed with mean 10.3 and standard deviation 2. In addition it is also necessary to allow a time of 2X minutes between completing the second stage and starting the third stage. Given that W, X and Y are independent, calculate the probabilities that

(a) the first two stages will be completed in under 30 minutes,

(b) the equipment will be completely assembled in under 120 minutes.

Solution

(a) The time taken to complete the first two stages is S = W + X. From the above we know that S is normally distributed with mean

$$E(S) = E(W) + E(X) = 15.4 + 25.8 = 41.2,$$

and variance $\quad Var(S) = Var(W) + Var(X) = 9 + 16 = 25.$

$$P(S < 30) = P\left(Z < \frac{30 - 41.2}{\sqrt{25}}\right) = P(Z < -2.24) = 0.013 \text{ to 3 decimal places.}$$

(b) The time taken to completion is T = W + X + 2X + Y = W + 3X + Y. It follows that W is normally distributed with mean

$$E(T) = E(W) + 3E(X) + E(Y) = 15.4 + 3 \times 25.8 + 10.3 = 103.1,$$

and variance $\quad Var(T) = Var(W) + 9Var(X) + Var(Y) = 9 + 9 \times 16 + 4 = 157.$

$$P(T < 120) = P\left(Z < \frac{120 - 103.1}{\sqrt{157}}\right) \approx P(Z < 1.35) = 0.911 \text{ to 3 decimal places.}$$

Exercise 2.4b

1. The times taken by two runners A and B to run 400 m races are independent and normally distributed random variables having means 51.8 s and 52.3 s, and standard deviations 0.3 s and 0.4 s, respectively. If the two runners compete in a 400 m race, find the probability that A will beat B.

2. In a certain country the heights of men are normally distributed with mean 172 cm and standard deviation 4 cm, and the heights of women are normally distributed with mean 164 cm and standard deviation 3 cm. If one man and one woman are chosen at random, find the probabilities that (a) the man is taller than the woman, (b) the woman's height is at least 90% of the man's height.

3. Cylindrical rods have diameters that are normally distributed with mean 35.4 mm and standard deviation 0.08 mm. The rods are to be inserted into circular holes whose diameters are normally distributed with mean 35.5 mm and standard deviation 0.01 mm. A satisfactory fit is obtained provided the hole diameter exceeds the rod diameter by between 0.04 mm and 0.05 mm. If a rod is chosen at random and is inserted into a randomly chosen hole, find the probability that a satisfactory fit will be obtained.

4. The weight of fruit delivered into a can is normally distributed with mean 250 g and standard deviation 1.2 g. The weight of an empty can is normally distributed with mean 25 g and standard deviation 0.5 g. Calculate (a) the mean and standard deviation of the weight of a filled can, (b) the probability that a filled can will weigh more than 278 g.

5. Hollow steel bases for wooden posts have rectangular cross-sections whose lengths and breadths are independent random variables, the lengths being normally distributed with mean 10 cm and standard deviation 0.4 cm, and the breadths being normally distributed with mean 6 cm and standard deviation 0.2 cm. The wooden posts have rectangular cross-sections whose lengths and breadths are independent normally distributed random variables, the lengths having mean 9.9 cm and standard deviation 0.3 cm, and the breadths having mean 5.9 cm and standard deviation 0.15 cm. Find the probability that a randomly chosen post will go into a randomly chosen steel base.

6. A salesperson is due to visit a certain town. Suppose that the time in hours that the salesperson will spend in the town is normally distributed with mean 5 and standard deviation 1.6. Independently of the time spent in the town, the time in hours taken to travel to the town and the time taken to return home are independent, each having a normal distribution with mean 1.2 and standard deviation 0.4. Find the probabilities that (a) the salesperson's time away from home will be less than 9 hours, (b) the time spent in town will be more than twice the time spent travelling.

7. Orange-flavoured sweets have weights which are normally distributed with mean 8 g and standard deviation 0.2 g. (a) Find the probability that the weight of the sweets in a packet containing 16 sweets will exceed 130 g. (b) Show that a packet should contain at least 26 sweets if there is to be a probability of at least 0.99 that the weight of the sweets in the packet will exceed 200 g. (c) The weights of lemon-flavoured sweets are normally distributed with mean 9 g and standard deviation 0.3 g. A packet of 10 sweets consists of 4 orange-flavoured sweets and 6 lemon-flavoured sweets. Find the probability that the weight of the sweets in the packet exceeds 88 g.

8. The weight, X g of a filled tin of soup is normally distributed with mean 560 and standard deviation 13. The weight, Y g, of an empty tin which is to contain soup is normally distributed with mean 30 and standard deviation 5. Let W g denote the weight of the soup in a tin.

(a) Which two of X, Y and W are independent?

(b) Find the mean and standard deviation of the weight of soup in a tin.

(c)   Calculate the probability that the weight of soup in a tin will be less than 500 g.

9.   The weights of persons using a lift are normally distributed with mean 68 kg and standard deviation 9 kg. The lift has a maximum permissible weight of 295 kg.

(a)   Find the probability that the maximum load is exceeded by four persons in the lift.

(b)   One man enters the lift carrying luggage equal to three times his weight. Find the probability that the maximum load is exceeded.

10.   The lengths of rods of type A are normally distributed with mean 5 cm and standard deviation 0.5 cm, while the lengths of rods of type B are normally distributed with mean 9 cm and standard deviation 1 cm. Find the probabilities that

(a)   the combined length of two rods of type A and one rod of type B will exceed 21 cm,

(b)   the combined length of two rods of type A and two rods of type B will exceed 31 cm,

(c)   the combined length of two rods of type A will be greater than the length of one rod of type B,

(d)   a type B rod will have a length that is more than twice the length of a type A rod.

11.   Every weekday morning both Aled and Berwyn arrive at a bus stop to catch the 8.00 am bus to their workplace. Aled's arrival time at the bus stop can be modelled by a normal distribution with mean 7.50 am and standard deviation 4 minutes. Independently, Berwyn's arrival time can be modelled by a normal distribution with mean 7.54 am and standard deviation 3 minutes. Calculate the probability that on a day

(a)   both Aled and Berwyn will arrive at the bus stop before 7.57 am,

(b)   Berwyn will arrive before Aled,

(c)   Aled and Berwyn will arrive within 2 minutes of each other.

2.5 Distribution of a sample mean

Let X denote a random variable associated with the outcomes of a random experiment which can be repeated indefinitely under identical conditions. For example, X could be the score obtained when a die is thrown or some numerical quality characteristic of a mass-produced item. Let $X_1, X_2, \ldots X_n$ denote the outcomes of n independent trials of the random experiment. Then $X_1, X_2, \ldots, X_n$ are independent random variables (since the trials are independent) and each has the same distribution as X. We refer to $X_1, X_2, \ldots, X_n$ as being a **random sample of n observations of X.**

Let $\overline{X}$ denote the mean of a random sample of n observations of a random variable X whose mean is μ and whose variance is σ^2. Observe that

$$\overline{X} = \frac{1}{n}(X_1 + X_2 + \ldots + X_n)$$

is a linear combination of n independent random variables. Hence, using the results given in the preceding section

$$E(\overline{X}) = \mu \text{ since } E(X_i) = \mu \text{ for } i = 1, 2, \ldots, n$$

and

$$Var(\overline{X}) = \frac{1}{n^2} \times n\sigma^2 \text{, since } Var(X_i) = \sigma^2 \text{ for } i = 1, 2, \ldots, n$$

$$= \sigma^2/n .$$

It follows that, for any random variable X having mean μ and variance σ^2, the distribution of $\overline{X}$ has mean μ and variance σ^2/n.

Furthermore, it follows from Section 2.4 that if X is normally distributed then so is $\overline{X}$ with mean and variance as given above. We therefore have the following important result:

$$\text{If } X \sim N(\mu, \sigma^2) \text{ then } \overline{X} \sim N(\mu, \sigma^2/n)$$

Example 1

The operational lifetimes, in hours, of light bulbs of a particular brand are normally distributed with mean 1060 and standard deviation 20.

(a) Calculate the probability that the mean lifetime of a random sample of 25 bulbs will be greater than 1050 hours.

(b) Find the smallest n for which there is a probability of at least 0·8 that the mean lifetime of a random sample of n bulbs will be greater than 1055 hours.

Solution

Let X hours denote the lifetime of a randomly chosen bulb, where $X \sim N(1060, 20^2)$.

(a) Let $\overline{X}$ denote the mean lifetime of a random sample of 25 bulbs. Using the above result we know that

$$\overline{X} \sim N(1060, \frac{400}{25}) \equiv N(1060, 4^2) .$$

Hence, on standardising, we have

$$P(\overline{X} > 1050) = P(Z > \frac{1050 - 1060}{4}) = P(Z > -2·5) = 0·9938.$$

(b) Let $\overline{X}$ denote the mean lifetime of a random sample of n bulbs. Then

$$\overline{X} \sim N(1060, \frac{400}{n}) .$$

We require the smallest n for which $P(\overline{X} > 1055) \geq 0\cdot8$, which is equivalent to

$$P(Z > \frac{1055 - 1060}{20/\sqrt{n}}) \geq 0\cdot8 \text{ or } P(Z > -\frac{\sqrt{n}}{4}) \equiv P(Z < \frac{\sqrt{n}}{4}) \geq 0\cdot8.$$

Referring to Table 4 we find that n must be such that

$$\frac{\sqrt{n}}{4} \geq 0\cdot842 \text{ or } n \geq (4 \times 0\cdot842)^2 \geq 11\cdot34 .$$

It follows that n should be at least 12.

Example 2

In an examination with a very large entry, the marks obtained by the male candidates were normally distributed with mean 56 and standard deviation 16, while the marks obtained by the female candidates were normally distributed with mean 61 and standard deviation 20. Let $\overline{X}$ denote the mean mark obtained by a random sample of 4 male candidates and let $\overline{Y}$ denote the mean mark obtained by a random sample of 5 female candidates. Calculate the probability that $\overline{Y} > \overline{X}$.

Solution

Using the result given above we know that

$$\overline{X} \sim N(56, 16^2/4) \text{ and } \overline{Y} \sim N(61, 20^2/5).$$

Clearly $\overline{X}$ and $\overline{Y}$ are independent and, since $\overline{Y} - \overline{X}$ is a linear combination of normally distributed random variables it follows from the above that

$$\overline{Y} - \overline{X} \sim N(61 - 56, 16^2/4 + 20^2/5) \text{ i.e. } N(5, 144) .$$

Hence, $P(\overline{Y} > \overline{X}) \equiv P(\overline{Y} - \overline{X} > 0) = P(Z > \frac{0 - 5}{12}) \approx P(Z > -0\cdot42) \approx 0.66$

Exercise 2.5

1. The random variable X is normally distributed with mean 58 and standard deviation 5. Find the probability that the mean of a random sample of 36 observations of X will (a) exceed 60, (b) lie between 56 and 59.

2. A random sample of 24 observations is taken from a normal distribution having mean 50 and variance 6. Find the probability that the sample mean will be (a) less than 48.5, (b) between 50.7 and 51.2.

3. In a certain county the men have heights that are normally distributed with mean 172 cm and standard deviation 10 cm. Calculate the probability that the mean of the heights of 4 randomly chosen men will be less than 180 cm.

4. The weights of turkeys on a turkey farm are normally distributed with mean 7 kg and standard deviation 1.5 kg. Calculate, to three decimal places, the probability that the mean weight of a random sample of 100 turkeys will lie between 6.85 kg and 7.4 kg.

5. An automatic packing machine fills bags with sugar in such a way that the mass of sugar in a randomly chosen bag is normally distributed with mean 1 kg and standard deviation 0.02 kg. To check the working of the machine, a sample of packets is taken and weighed. The whole batch is accepted if the mean mass of the sample is within 5 grams of the nominal mass of 1 kg. How large a sample should be taken if the probability of acceptance is to be at least 0.9 when the machine is working properly?

6. When a certain instrument is used to measure a length, it is known that the error is normally distributed with mean 0 and standard deviation 0.5 mm.

   (a) In 4 independent applications of the instrument calculate the probability that the mean error will be **numerically** less than 0.05 mm.

   (b) If the instrument is applied n times find the least value of n for the probability to be at least 0.9 that the mean error will be **numerically** less than 0.1 mm.

7. The wages paid to the weekly-paid staff of a large factory are normally distributed with mean £120.50 and standard deviation £6. (a) Calculate the probability that the mean weekly wage of a random sample of 9 of the weekly-paid staff will be greater than £125. (b) How large a random sample should be taken if there is to be a probability of approximately 0.9 that the sample mean wage will be within £2 of the population mean wage of £120.50?

8. Random variables X and Y are such that $X \sim N(100, 12)$ and $Y \sim N(120, 20)$. Random samples of 50 observations of each of X and Y are taken. Calculate the probability that the mean value of the 50 observations of Y will be at least 21 more than the mean value of the 50 observations of X.

9. In a certain country the heights of girls and boys aged 16 years are normally distributed. The girls' height have mean 162.5 cm and standard deviation 4.0 cm, while the boys' heights have mean 173.5 cm and standard deviation 4.8 cm. Let $\overline{X}$ and $\overline{Y}$ respectively, denote the mean heights of a random sample of 64 girls and a random sample of 36 boys.

   (a) Write down the sampling distributions of (i) $\overline{X}$, (ii) $\overline{Y}$, (iii) $\overline{Y} - \overline{X}$.

   (b) Calculate correct to two decimal places, the probability that $\overline{Y}$ will have a value which is at least 12 cm greater than the value of $\overline{X}$.

10. The distance, in km, travelled per week by a motorist is normally distributed with mean 1024 and standard deviation 80.

(a) Calculate, correct to two decimal places, the probability that the average distance travelled per week by this motorist over a period of a year (52 weeks) will be greater than 1040 km.

(b) The car's petrol consumption is 10.6 km per litre. Calculate, correct to two decimal places, the probability that this motorist will require less than 360 litres of petrol over a period of 4 weeks.

Miscellaneous Questions on Chapter 2

1. (A3 1988) The random variables X and Y are independent and have the following probability distributions.

x	1	2
P(X=x)	0.4	0.6

y	1	2	3
P(Y=y)	0. 3	0. 4	0. 3

(i) Evaluate $E(\dfrac{Y}{X})$. [3]

Let $U = XY$ and $W = 2X - Y$.

(ii) Show that $E(UW) = E(U)E(W)$ [6]

(iii) Evaluate $P(U=2, W=0)$ [2]

2. (A3 1989) A double glazing salesperson canvasses customers to purchase replacement windows and patio doors.. The salesperson receives a commission of 10% of the total order value for replacement windows, and a commission of 15% of the total order value for patio doors. In any month, the salesperson's total order value for replacement windows is a random variable having mean £2500 and standard deviation £500, and, independently, the salesperson's total order value for patio doors is a random variable having mean £1200 and standard deviation £250. Find the mean and the standard deviation of this salesperson's total monthly commission. [5]

3. (A3 1989) The numbers, X and Y, of two types of bacteria A and B, respectively, in a given volume of a solution are independent random variables having Poisson distributions. The mean number of type A bacteria per litre of the solution is 3.6, while the mean number of type B bacteria per litre is 1. 24.

(a) Find, correct to three decimal places, the probabilities that a sample of 1 litre of the solution will contain (i) exactly 4 bacteria of type A, (ii) 3 or fewer bacteria of type B, (iii) exactly 2 bacteria of type A and exactly 2 bacteria of type B.   [7]

(b) Let W = XY. (i) Find, correct to three decimal places, the probability that for a sample of 1 litre of the solution the value of W is zero.   [4]

(ii) Evaluate the mean and the variance of W.   [4]

4. (A3 1989) A garage stocks two brands, A and B, of car batteries. The lifetimes, X months, of brand A batteries may be assumed to be distributed as $N(\mu, \sigma^2)$.

(i) Given that 1% of brand A batteries last less than 40 months and that 25% last more than 46 months, find the values of μ and σ; give your answers correct to two decimal places   [5]

The lifetimes, Y months, of brand B batteries may be assumed to be normally distributed with mean 40 and standard deviation 4. A particular person always buys a replacement car battery from the garage. Given the choice, this person will buy a brand A battery but will accept a brand B battery if only brand B batteries are in stock at the time. Suppose that at any point in time the probability of the garage having only brand B batteries in stock is 0.6.

(ii) Calculate the probability that a battery bought by the above person at the garage will last for more than 46 months.   [4]

(iii) Let T_A denote the sum of the lifetimes of a random sample of 5 batteries of brand A and let T_B denote the sum of the lifetimes of a random sample of 6 batteries of brand B. Taking the mean (μ) and the standard deviation (σ) of the lifetimes of brand A batteries to be 45 months and 2 months, respectively, calculate the probability that T_A and T_B will not differ by more than 10 months.   [6]

5. (A3 1990) The random variable X has the Poisson distribution with mean 0.4. Independently of X, the random variable Y has the distribution shown in the following table.

y	0	1	2
P(Y=y)	0.2	0.6	0.2

(i) State the variance of X and show that Y has the same variance.

(ii) Let T = 2Y – X and U = Y + 2X. Verify that E(TU) = E(T)E(U).   [7]

6. (A3 1990) A machine is used to bag coal, the mass of coal delivered per bag being normally distributed with mean 55 kg and standard deviation 1.25 kg.

(b) Given two bags chosen at random calculate the probabilities that (i) each bag contains at least 56 kg, (ii) the combined mass of coal in the two bags is less than 112 kg,

(iii) one bag contains at least 1 kg more than the other bag, (iv) the heavier of the two bags contains more than 57 kg. [12]

7. (A3 1992) A newsagent stocks copies of two gardening magazines, *Gardening News* and *Today's Garden*, both of which are published monthly. In any month, the number of customers requiring the current issue of *Gardening News* has the Poisson distribution with mean 10 and, independently, the number requiring the current issue of *Today's Garden* has the Poisson distribution with mean 5. In each month the newsagent has only 10 copies of *Gardening News* and only 5 copies of *Today's Garden* available for sale.

(a) Find (i) the most probable number of copies of *Today's Garden* that will be **sold** in a month, (ii) the mean value, correct to two decimal places, of the number of copies of *Today's Garden* **sold** per month. [7]

(b) Find, correct to three decimal places, the probability that in a month the newsagent will (i) sell exactly 5 copies of *Gardening News* and exactly 4 copies of *Today's Garden*, (ii) not be able to supply the magazine of the choice of at least one customer. [8]

8. (A3 1992) The heights of the male students at a large college are normally distributed with mean 180 cm and standard deviation 4 cm. Independently, the heights of the female students at the college are normally distributed with mean 170 cm and standard deviation 5 cm

(a) If one male student and one female student are chosen at random evaluate the probability that (i) both will be taller than 175 cm, (ii) the female student will be taller than the male student. [7]

(b) If two male students and three female students are chosen at random evaluate the probability that the sum of the heights of all five students will be greater than 850 cm. [3]

9. (A3 1993) The number of days in a term that a randomly chosen boy will be absent from school has a Poisson distribution with mean 2 and independently, the number of days in a term that a randomly chosen girl will be absent from school has a Poisson distribution with mean 3.

(b) One boy and one girl are chosen at random. Find, correct to three decimal places, the probability that in a term one of them will be absent for 2 days and the other will be absent for 3 days. [4]

10. (S1 Jan 1996) An office block has a lift whose maximum permitted load is 500 kg. It is known that the weights of the men and women using the lift can be modelled by normal distributions. The men's weights have mean 80 kg and standard deviation

12 kg. The women's weights have mean 56 kg and standard deviation 6 kg. On one occasion, 3 men and 4 women enter the lift. Calculate, correct to two significant figures, the probability that

(a) their combined weight exceeds the maximum permitted load, [4]

(b) the combined weight of the 3 men exceeds that of the 4 women. [4]

11.(S1 June 1996) The random variables X and Y are independent and each has a Poisson distribution with mean μ.

(a) Show that $E(X^2) = \mu(\mu + 1)$ [2]

(b) Given that $Z = XY$, show that $Var(Z) = \mu^2(2\mu + 1)$. [3]

12. (A3 1996) Four athletes run a 4×400 m relay race. Their coach knows from past experience that the times taken for each athlete to complete her 400 m leg are normally distributed with the following means and standard deviations.

Athlete	Mean (sec)	S.D. (sec)
1	57.3	1.3
2	63.5	1.7
3	60.9	1.5
4	59.8	1.9

(a) Calculate the mean and standard deviation of the total time taken by the athletes to complete the four legs, stating clearly where any assumption concerning independence is required.
[4]

(b) Calculate the probability that the four legs are completed in a total time of less than 4 minutes. [3]

13. (S1 June 1996) Faults occur at random in the manufacture of a certain cable at a mean rate of 3.75 per 100 m. Lengths of this cable are wound onto drums, each drum carrying 40 m. If X represents the number of faults occurring on a drum, write down an appropriate model for the distribution of X. [1]

(a) Find, without the use of tables, the probability that there are at least 2 faults on a drum. [2]

(b) A customer buys 5 drums. Find the probability that exactly 3 of them have at least 2 faults. [2]

(c) Another customer buys 100 drums. Find, approximately, the probability that these drums contain between them at least 175 faults. Give your answer correct to three decimal places. [4]

14. (A3 1996) Independently for each day, the daily number of machine breakdowns in a factory can be modelled by the Poisson distribution with mean 2.5.

(b) Calculate the probability that at least 20 breakdowns occur in a 6-day week.   [2]

(c) Use a distributional approximation to calculate the probability that at least 780 breakdowns occur in a 300-day year.   [4]

15. (A3 1997) The weights of pieces of home-made toffee are normally distributed with mean 35 grams and standard deviation 4 grams.

(b) A bag of nominal weight 200 grams contains 6 pieces of toffee. Calculate the probability that the total weight of toffee in the bag exceeds the nominal weight.   [4]

16. (S1 June 1999) Every weekday morning buses depart from a village to a neighbouring town at 07.00, 07.30, and 08.00. On any morning the numbers of passengers using these buses have independent Poisson distributions with means 4, 11 and 34, respectively.

(b) Find the probability that on a weekday morning the combined total number of passengers using the buses leaving at 07.00 and 07.30 will be at least 10.   [2]

(c) Find an approximate value for the probability that on a weekday morning the combined total number of passengers using all three buses will be 38 or fewer.   [4]

17. (S1 Jan 1999) In the first draft of a Statistics book, two kinds of typographical errors may occur. One kind of error occurs in the words and the other kind occurs in the mathematical formulae used. The number of errors in the words in n pages has the Poisson distribution with mean 0.65n and, independently, the number of errors in the formulae in n pages has the Poisson distribution with mean 0.25n.

(b) Given that the book contains 250 pages, find an approximate value for the probability that the combined number of errors in the words and the formulae will be less than 230.   [5]

18. (S1 Jan 1999) A newsagent sells National Lottery tickets and Instant Cash tickets. The newsagent's weekly takings from the sale of National Lottery tickets is a random variable X whose distribution may be modelled by a normal distribution having mean £450 and standard deviation £20. Independently, the weekly takings from the sale of Instant Cash tickets is a random variable Y whose distribution may be modelled by a normal distribution having mean £120 and standard deviation £15.

(a) Calculate the probability that in a week the newsagent's total takings from the sale of National Lottery tickets and Instant Cash tickets will exceed £600.   [3]

(b) Assuming that the total takings in any week is independent of the total takings in any other week, calculate the probability that in a period of four weeks the newsagent's total takings from the sale of National Lottery tickets and Instant Cash tickets will be less than £2200. [3]

(c) Calculate the probability that in a week the newsagent's takings from the sale of National Lottery tickets will be more than three times the takings from the sale of Instant Cash tickets.

19. (S1 June 1999) The mass, X grams, of jam in a jar is normally distributed with mean 454 and standard deviation 5. The combined mass, T grams, of a jar and its contents is normally distributed with mean 620 and standard deviation 8. Let Y grams denote the mass of an empty jar.

(c) Which two of X, Y and T are independent random variables? [1]

(d) Giving a clear indication of your working, determine the mean and the variance of Y (the mass of an empty jar). [3]

Chapter 3

Hypothesis Testing 1

Introduction

Examine any coin you have. Can you tell whether or not it is unbiased in the sense that when tossed a head and a tail are equally likely to occur? Your response (in common with others including experts in mechanics) is undoubtedly "No". The question posed is equivalent to that of deciding whether or not the probability of a head in one toss of the coin is equal to $\frac{1}{2}$. This may prompt you to recall the definition of the probability of any event associated with a random experiment as being the relative frequency of the event in an indefinitely large number of trials of the random experiment. But this is of no practical use since it is not possible to carry out an indefinitely large number of tosses of the coin. The best one can do is to toss the coin a specified number of times, say n times, and count the number of tosses which gave a head. Let X denote the number of heads that will be obtained in n tosses of the coin. Then X/n, the relative frequency of heads, will provide an estimate of the probability of a head in a future toss of the coin.

Recall that X has the binomial distribution B(n,p), where p is the probability of a head and that $E(X) = np$. If the coin is unbiased so that $p = \frac{1}{2}$ then $E(X) = \frac{1}{2}n$. If the observed value of X should turn out to be much larger or much smaller than $\frac{1}{2}n$ then we would tend to conclude that the coin is biased. But note that whatever the value of p, X may take any one of the values 0,1,2,…,n, so that even when the coin is unbiased a value of X very different from $\frac{1}{2}n$ is possible. Thus, it is clear that there is no way in which we can with certainty decide whether or not the coin is unbiased.

A method will be described later for reaching a conclusion which will provide some protection (probabilistically) against concluding that the coin is biased when, in fact, the coin is unbiased. Before describing this method we need to introduce some terminology.

3.1 Null and alternative hypotheses

Let X denote a random variable whose distribution depends on an unknown quantity θ (referred to as a **parameter** of the distribution). Instances arise in practice where a random sample of observations of X is to be used to test whether or not θ has the particular value θ_0. (In the situation described in the above introduction we had just one observation X from the binomial distribution B(n,θ) where θ is the probability of a head and the particular value of interest was $\theta_0 = \frac{1}{2}$).

The assertion $\theta = \theta_0$ is referred to as the **null hypothesis** and will be abbreviated as H_0: $\theta = \theta_0$. Having set up an appropriate H_0 the next step is to specify the **alternative hypothesis**, denoted by H_1, that is to be accepted if it is decided to reject H_0. (In the problem discussed in the introduction above the null hypothesis would be H_0: $\theta = \frac{1}{2}$ (i.e. the coin is unbiased) and the alternative hypothesis would be H_1: $\theta \neq \frac{1}{2}$ (i.e. the coin is biased). In general the alternative hypothesis may take any one of the following three forms.

1. H_1: $\theta < \theta_0$. This form of alternative will be appropriate when one knows before taking the sample that θ is at most θ_0 or when one is only interested in detecting a value of θ which is less than θ_0. For example, let μ_0 be the mean number of accidents that have occurred per month on a particular motorway. It has been suggested that installing speed cameras along the motorway would reduce the accident rate. Letting μ denote the mean number of accidents that will occur after installing the speed cameras, the appropriate null and alternative hypotheses are H_0: $\mu = \mu_0$ and H_1: $\mu < \mu_0$.

2. H_1: $\theta > \theta_0$. This form of alternative will be appropriate when one knows before taking the sample that θ is at least θ_0 or when one is only interested in detecting a value of θ which is greater than θ_0. As an example, suppose that μ_0 is the current mean quality of certain mass-produced items. A modification to the manufacturing process has been proposed which is thought will increase the mean quality. In this case the appropriate null and alternative hypotheses are H_0: $\mu = \mu_0$ and H_1: $\mu > \mu_0$.

3. H_1: $\theta \neq \theta_0$. This alternative is appropriate when one has no prior information on the value of θ, or when one is interested in detecting a value of θ which is different from θ_0 in either direction. This is the appropriate form when testing whether or not a coin is unbiased, where θ is the probability of a head and $\theta_0 = \frac{1}{2}$.

An alternative hypothesis of the form H_1: $\theta < \theta_0$ or H_1; $\theta > \theta_0$ is said to be **one-sided**, while one of the form H_1: $\theta \neq \theta_0$ is said to be **two-sided**.

[In an examination the wording of any question on hypothesis testing should be such that it is clear from the context which form of alternative hypothesis is appropriate. If not, it is advisable to clearly state the form of alternative hypothesis you have chosen].

Exercise 3.1

In each of the following, identify the parameter of interest and set up appropriate null and alternative hypotheses.

1. A certain drug is known to cure 75% of patients treated. A new drug is to be tried on a sample of patients to see if it has a higher cure rate.

2. A cubical die is to be thrown several times to test if it is biased against giving a score of 6.

3. A motorist has found over a long period of time that his car's average fuel consumption is 11·7 km per litre. The motorist fits a gadget to the car which is claimed to reduce the average fuel consumption.

4. When a machine is operating correctly it produces steel pins having a mean length of 2·5 cm. Samples of the pins are taken periodically to check that the mean length has not changed.

5. In the last general election, 40% of the voters in a particular constituency voted Labour. A month prior to the next general election it is proposed to conduct a sample poll of the voters to test if the percentage voting for Labour has changed from the time of the last election.

3.2 The p-value

Let $X_1, X_2, \ldots, X_n$ denote a random sample of n observations of the random variable X whose distribution depends on the parameter θ and that the sample is to be used to test the null hypothesis $H_0: \theta = \theta_0$. Let T denote a combination of $X_1, X_2, \ldots, X_n$ which is deemed suitable for the test. For example, if θ is the distribution mean μ, then a suitable choice of T would be the sample mean $\overline{X}$. The chosen T is referred to as the **test statistic**. Note that T is itself a random variable. A decision on whether or not the null hypothesis should be rejected is to be based on the observed value t of T. What is required is a measure of how likely or unlikely it is that the observed t is a reasonable value for T if the null hypothesis is true. One such measure is the **p-value** defined as follows:

Definition: Given the observed value t of T, the p-value is the probability that T will have a value **at least as extreme** as t if the null hypothesis is true.

It is clear from this definition that the p-value can be calculated only if we know the distribution of T when the null hypothesis is true.

A calculated p-value of p_0, say, means that $100p_0\%$ of all possible samples of the size to be taken will have a value of T which is at least as extreme as the observed t. The smaller the p-value the stronger is the sample evidence that H_0 is false. Deciding on how small a p-value, should be to justify rejecting H_0 will depend on the seriousness of the consequences of wrongfully rejecting H_0. When it is not possible to assess these consequences a rule that is commonly used is to reject H_0 only if the p-value is less than or equal to 0·05. A more detailed set of guidelines for interpreting p-values is as follows.

(a) If the p-value is ≤ 0.01 the sample provided very strong evidence for rejecting H_0.

(b) If $0.01 <$ the p-value ≤ 0.05 the sample provided strong evidence for rejecting H_0.

(c) If the p-value is > 0.05 there is insufficient evidence to justify rejecting H_0.

Note well that (c) does not permit one to conclude that H_0 is true. This is as it should be since the precise value of the parameter θ is unknown and will still be unknown even after the sample observations become available. In this sense the above procedure is somewhat one-sided in that it provides probabilistic protection against the wrongful rejection of H_0 but does not allow for the acceptance of H_0 as being true. The procedure has been devised to deal with situations where the purpose is to detect a deviation from the hypothesised value θ_0.

Before applying the above procedure to specific cases we need to explain precisely what is meant by "at least as extreme" in the definition of the p-value. In the cases we shall be considering the distribution of T is such that $E(T) = k\theta$, where k is a positive constant. In particular, on assuming H_0 to be true, $E(T) = k\theta_0$.

If the alternative hypothesis is $H_1: \theta < \theta_0$ then an extreme value of T is one which is small compared with $k\theta_0$, so that in this case

$$\text{the p-value} = P(T \leq t \text{ when } H_0 \text{ is true}).$$

Similarly, if the alternative hypothesis is $H_1: \theta > \theta_0,$ an extreme value of T is one which is large compared with $k\theta_0$, and

$$\text{the p-value} = P(T \geq t \text{ when } H_0 \text{ is true}).$$

When H_1 is two-sided i.e. $\theta \neq \theta_0$ an extreme value of T will be one which is either large or small compared with $k\theta_0$. Now the observed value t of T will either be $< k\theta_0$ or $> k\theta_0$. Whichever of these occurs we need to allow for a **probabilistically** equally extreme value in the other direction from $k\theta_0$. It follows that in this case the p-value will be as follows.

(a) for $t > k\theta_0$, the p-value $= 2P(T \geq t \text{ when } H_0 \text{ is true})$,

(b) for $t < k\theta_0$, the p-value $= 2P(T \leq t \text{ when } H_0 \text{ is true})$.

The following subsections illustrate the above procedure in some standard situations.

3.2.1. Testing the mean of a normal distribution of known variance

Consider a random variable X which is normally distributed with unknown mean μ and known variance σ^2. A random sample of n observations is to be used to test $H_0 : \mu = \mu_0$ for some specific value μ_0. In this case an obvious choice of test statistic is $\overline{X}$, whose distribution is known to be normal with mean μ and standard deviation $\sigma/\sqrt{n}$. It follows that when H_0 is assumed to be true, $\overline{X} \sim N(\mu_0, \sigma^2/n)$. Let $\overline{x}$ be the observed value of $\overline{X}$ obtained from the sample.

CASE A : Testing $H_0 : \mu = \mu_0$ against $H_1 : \mu > \mu_0$.

Here, an extreme value of $\overline{X}$ is one which is large compared with μ_0 and therefore,

the p-value $= P(\overline{X} \geq \overline{x}$ when H_0 is true)

$$= P\left(Z \geq \frac{\overline{x} - \mu_0}{SD(\overline{X})}\right) \qquad (1)$$

where $SD(\overline{X}) = \sigma/\sqrt{n}$ and $Z \sim N(0, 1)$.

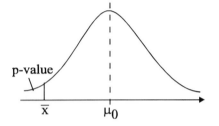

CASE B : Testing $H_0 : \mu = \mu_0$ against $H_1 : \mu < \mu_0$.

In this case it follows that

the p-value $= P(\overline{X} \leq \overline{x}$ when H_0 is true)

$$= P\left(Z \leq \frac{\overline{x} - \mu_0}{SD(\overline{X})}\right) \qquad (2)$$

CASE C : Testing $H_0 : \mu = \mu_0$ against $H_1 : \mu \neq \mu_0$.

In this case an extreme value of $\overline{X}$ may be one which is large or small compared with μ_0.

(a) If $\overline{x}$ is $> \mu_0$, then allowing for an equally extreme value which is $< \mu_0$,

the p-value $= 2P(\overline{X} \geq \overline{x}$ when H_0 is true) $= 2P\left(Z \geq \frac{\overline{x} - \mu_0}{SD(\overline{X})}\right)$

(b) If $\overline{x}$ is $< \mu_0$, then allowing for an equally extreme value which is $> \mu_0$,

the p-value $= 2P(\overline{X} \leq \overline{x}$ when H_0 is true) $= 2P\left(Z \leq \frac{\overline{x} - \mu_0}{SD(\overline{X})}\right)$

Example 1

Nylon cord produced by a certain manufacturer is known to be such that one-metre lengths have breaking strengths that are normally distributed with mean 10.2 kg and standard deviation 0.8 kg. Laboratory experiments have indicated that a modification to the manufacturing process will give breaking strengths that are normally distributed with an increased mean but the same standard deviation. The modified process was used to produce 25 one-metre lengths and it was found that the sample mean breaking strength was 10.4 kg. Test the hypothesis that the modification will not change the mean breaking strength against the alternative that it will give a higher mean breaking strength.

Solution

Let X kg denote the breaking strength of a nylon cord from the modified process, and let μ kg denote the mean breaking strength of such cords. Then, $X \sim N(\mu, 0.8^2)$. We need to test

$H_0 : \mu = 10.2$ against $H_1 : \mu > 10.2$.

Let $\overline{X}$ denote the mean of a random sample of 25 cords from the modified process. Then $\overline{X}$ is normally distributed with mean μ and standard deviation $0.8/5 = 0.16$. Since the observed sample mean is 10.4,

$$\text{the p-value} = P(\overline{X} \geq 10.4 \text{ when } \mu = 10.2)$$
$$= P\left(Z \geq \frac{10.4 - 10.2}{0.16}\right)$$
$$= P(Z \geq 1.25) \approx 0.1056$$

p-value

10.2 10.4

Since the p-value is > 0.05 there is insufficient evidence to justify rejecting H_0; that is, there is insufficient evidence to conclude that the modified process will produce cords of higher mean breaking strength. [Since the p-value is not particularly large, we could recommend that a larger sample of cords be taken from the modified process for a more reliable assessment.]

Example 2

The mean distance travelled per week by a long-distance driver has been 1130 km. In the first 20 weeks following the introduction of new driving regulations he drove a total of 21600 km. Assuming that the distance travelled per week after the introduction of the new driving regulations is normally distributed with standard deviation 106 km, test whether the mean weekly distance travelled has changed from the previous figure of 1130 km.

Solution

Let X km denote the distance travelled in a week following the introduction of the new driving regulations and denote the mean distance travelled by μ. Then X has the normal distribution $N(\mu, 106^2)$. We need to test

$$H_0: \mu = 1130 \text{ (previous mean)} \quad v \quad H_1: \mu \neq 1130 \text{ (changed mean)}$$

Let $\overline{X}$ denote the mean distance travelled in 20 weeks. Assuming that H_0 is true

$$\overline{X} \sim N(1130, \frac{106^2}{20} = 561{\cdot}8).$$

The observed value $\overline{x} = \frac{21600}{20} = 1080$, which is less than $E(\overline{X}) = 1130$.

Since H_1 is two-sided

$$\text{the p-value} = 2P(\overline{X} \leq 1080) = 2P(Z < \frac{1080 - 1130}{\sqrt{561.8}})$$

$$= 2P(Z < -2{\cdot}11) = 2 \times 0{\cdot}01743 \approx 0{\cdot}035.$$

Since the p-value is less than 0·05 but greater than 0·01 there is strong evidence against H_0 so we can conclude that there has been a change in the mean distance travelled. Since the observed $\bar{x}$ is less than E(X) we can be more positive and conclude that the mean distance travelled after the introduction of the new driving regulations is less than the previous mean distance travelled.

Exercise 3.2.1

1. A random sample of 25 observations is taken from a normal distribution having mean μ and standard deviation 2 in order to test $H_0 : \mu = 10$ against $H_1 : \mu > 10$. Carry out the test given that the observed sample mean was 11.

2. When a machine is operating correctly it produces steel pins whose lengths are normally distributed with mean 2.5 cm and standard deviation 0.05 cm. Any malfunction of the machine affects only the mean length. Samples are taken periodically in order to check that the machine is operating correctly. Each such sample consists of 40 pins. Carry out a test to determine if the machine is malfunctioning given that the sample mean was (a) 2.49 cm, (b) 2.52 cm.

3. A company manufacturing electric light bulbs has a research section for developing modifications to the manufacturing process aimed at increasing the mean lifetime of the bulbs. At present the lifetimes are normally distributed with mean 2200 hours and standard deviation 118 hours. It may be assumed that any modification to the present process will affect the mean lifetime only. Any modification is used to produce 100 bulbs. Test whether a modification should be adopted given that the mean lifetime of the 100 bulbs was (a) 2210 hours, (b) 2231 hours.

4. Items produced by a certain machine have masses that are normally distributed with mean μ kg and standard deviation 0.02 kg. If $\mu \neq 1$ then the machine setting should be corrected. Given that the mean mass of a random sample of 25 items was 0.989 kg determine whether consideration should be given to correcting the machine-setting.

5. The tar yields in cigarettes of a particular brand are known to be normally distributed with mean μ mg and standard deviation 0.8 mg. In a random sample of 10 cigarettes the tar yields were found to be :
   17.1, 19.2, 18.3, 18.2, 18.9, 17.8, 17.8, 18.3, 16.9, 18.5
   Test the hypothesis that $\mu = 17.5$ against the alternative that $\mu > 17.5$.

3.2.2 Testing a probability or proportion

Let θ denote the unknown probability of a success in each trial of a random experiment. Suppose that it is required to test the null hypothesis $H_0 : \theta = \theta_0$, for some specified value θ_0, based on the number X of successes that will be obtained in n independent trials of the experiment. Assuming that H_0 is true, the distribution of X is $B(n, \theta_0)$ and the expected value of X is $E(X) = n\theta_0$. Thus, an observed value x of X which is very different from $n\theta_0$ will cast doubt on the validity of H_0.

CASE A : Testing $H_0 : \theta = \theta_0$ against $H_1 : \theta > \theta_0$.

In this case an extreme value of X is one which is large compared with $n\theta_0$, so that if the observed value of X is x

$$\text{the p-value } = \text{ P}(X \geq x \text{ when } H_0 \text{ is true})$$

CASE B : Testing $H_0 : \theta = \theta_0$ against $H_1 : \theta < \theta_0$.

An extreme value of X is now one which is small compared with $n\theta_0$, so that if x is the observed value of X,

$$\text{the p-value } = \text{ P}(X \leq x \text{ when } H_0 \text{ is true}).$$

CASE C : Testing $H_0 : \theta = \theta_0$ against $H_1 : \theta \neq \theta_0$.

An extreme value of X is now one which is large or small compared with $n\theta_0$. If the observed x is $> n\theta_0$ we have to allow for a probabilistically equally extreme value $< n\theta_0$, and if $x < n\theta_0$ we have to allow for a probabilistically equally extreme value $> n\theta_0$. Hence, the p-value is obtained as follows.

(a) If $x > n\theta_0$, the p-value $= 2\text{P}(X \geq x$ when H_0 is true)

(b) If $x < n\theta_0$, the p-value $= 2\text{P}(X \leq x$ when H_0 is true)

Example 1

The manufacturer of a new type of seeding compost claims that seeds sown in this new compost will have a higher germination rate than if they were sown in ordinary compost. For a particular variety of seed sown in ordinary compost the germination rate is known to be 0.7 (70%). To test the manufacturer's claim an experiment was conducted in which 20 of the seeds were sown in the new compost. Carry out the test, given that 18 of the 20 seeds germinated.

Solution

Let X denote the number of the 20 seeds sown in the new compost which will germinate and let θ denote the germination rate. Then $X \sim B(20, \theta)$. Since we are only interested in the possibility that $\theta > 0.7$ the appropriate null and alternative hypotheses are :

$$H_0 : \theta = 0.7 \text{ and } H_1 : \theta > 0.7.$$

Since the observed value of X is x = 18,

the p-value = $P(X \geq 18$ when H_0 is true)

If H_0 is true then $X \sim B(20, 0.7)$. Table 1 gives cumulative binomial probabilities for n = 20 only for values of $\theta \leq 0.5$. To enable us to use Table 1, let X' denote the number of the 20 seeds that will not germinate so that when H_0 is true $X' \sim B(20, 0.3)$. Now $X \geq 18$ is equivalent to $X' \leq 2$ so that, on referring to Table 1 we have

the p-value = $P(X' \leq 2) = 0.0355$.

It follows that the experiment provides strong evidence against H_0 so the conclusion is to support the claim made by the manufacturer.

Example 2

A supermarket claimed that 25% of its customers pay by credit card. Test this claim in each of the following cases.

(a) In a random sample of 50 customers it was found that 9 of them paid by credit card.

(b) In a random sample of 160 customers it was found that 28 of them paid by credit card.

Solution

Let θ denote the true proportion of the customers who pay by credit card. Since here we are interested in a value of θ which differs from 0.25 in either direction the appropriate null and alternative hypotheses are :

$$H_0 : \theta = 0.25 \quad \text{and} \quad H_1 : \theta \neq 0.25$$

We can treat payments by customers as being independent trials in each of which the probability of a success is θ, a success being payment by credit card. Let X denote the number of customers in a random sample of n customers who pay by credit card. Then $X \sim B(n, \theta)$.

(a) Here, if H_0 is true, $X \sim B(50, 0.25)$ whose expected value is 12.5. Since the observed value x = 9 is less than 12.5 and H_1 is two-sided,

the p-value = $2P(X \leq 9) = 2 \times 0.1637$ from Table 1

$= 0.3274$

This is much too large a p-value to justify rejecting H_0. So, on the basis of this sample there is insufficient evidence for disputing the claim made.

(b) In this case, if H_0 is true, $X \sim B(160, 0.25)$, whose mean is 40. Since the observed value x = 28 is less than 40 and H_1 is two-sided

the p-value = $2P(X \leq 28)$.

Since n = 160 is not included in Table 1 but is large and $\theta = 0.25$ is not close to 0 or 1 we can use the normal approximation with continuity correction to find an approximation to the p-value. The distribution B(160, 0.25) has mean 40 and variance $40 \times 0.75 = 30$ so that the approximating normal distribution is N(40, 30). On applying the continuity correction we have

$$\text{the p-value} = 2P(X \leq 28) \equiv 2P(X \leq 28.5)$$

$$\approx 2P\left(Z \leq \frac{28.5 - 40}{\sqrt{30}}\right) \approx 2P(Z \leq -2.10)$$

$$\approx 2 \times 0.0179 = 0.0358.$$

In this case the sample provides strong evidence against H_0 and, since the observed x was less than the expected value of 40 if H_0 were true, we conclude that the proportion of the customers who pay by credit card is less than 25%.

Exercise 3.2.2

1. A lady claimed that she can do better than guessing the suit of a playing card by touch alone. To test her claim, she was blindfolded and asked to identify the suits of 10 playing cards. Test her claim given that she correctly identified the suits of 5 of the cards.

2. It is suspected that a cheap imported die is biased. In 15 throws of the die a 6 occurred once only. Determine whether this information provides sufficient evidence to conclude that the die is biased.

3. The makers of the washing-up liquid 'Sparkle' claim that 35% of all housewives use their product, whereas this figure is disputed by a competitor as being an overestimate. In a random sample of 20 housewives it was found that 4 of them used 'Sparkle'. Test the claim made by the makers of 'Sparkle' against the claim made by the competitor.

4. The probability that an oyster larva will develop in unpolluted water is 0.9, while in polluted water this probability is less than 0.9. An oyster breeder put 20 larvae in a sample of water and observed that 16 of them developed. Test whether the breeder would be justified in concluding that the water used is polluted.

5. A certain drug is known to cure 55% of patients treated. In a clinical test, 10 patients were given a modified version of the drug which is claimed to be more effective. Given that 8 of the 10 patients were cured is one justified in concluding that the modification is more effective?

6. A gambler claimed that he could throw a fair die in such a way that his probability of throwing a 6 was greater than 1/6. To demonstrate his claim he threw a fair die 50 times and obtained a 6 in 12 of them. Determine whether his demonstration supports his claim.

7. Alan claims that he is a better tennis player than Bill and challenges Bill to a series of games. Test Alan's claim in each of the cases when

(a) Alan won 7 of the first 10 games played,

(b) Alan won 15 of the first 20 games played.

8. A coin is so damaged that it is not possible to judge whether it is fair. Test the unbiasedness of the coin in each of the following cases, giving a clear statement of your conclusion.

(a) In 20 tosses of the coin a head was obtained 14 times,

(b) In 120 tosses of the coin a head was obtained 72 times.

9. In a random sample of 200 adults residing in a certain region it was found that 120 of them were in favour of fluoridation of the domestic water supply. Test the hypothesis that 55% of the adults in the region favour fluoridation against the alternative that the proportion in favour is more than 55%.

10. A leaf disease was reported to affect 25% of all beech trees. A botanist suspects that the incidence of the disease increases with the degree of atmospheric pollution and conducted a survey of beech trees in an urban area. The botanist found 36 infected trees out of 120 examined. Test the botanist's suspicion.

11. A drug company claims in an advertisement that 60% of people suffering from a certain complaint gain instant relief by using their product. A doctor who felt that the claim was rather optimistic gave the product to 200 patients suffering from the complaint and found that 106 of them did gain instant relief. Use this information to test the validity of the advertised claim against the doctor's suspicion that the claim is optimistic.

12. A regular visitor to a casino suspected that the roulette wheel was unfair. On each spin of the wheel there are 37 possible scores, labelled 0 to 36, and all should have the same chance of occurring in any spin. The casino wins if the number 0 comes up. The visitor made a note of the numbers that came up in 740 spins of the wheel and found that the number 0 came up 35 times. Do these results provide sufficient evidence that the wheel gives an unfair advantage to the casino?

13. The random variable X is uniformly distributed over the interval $(-\theta, 2)$, where θ is an unknown positive constant. Find, in terms of θ, the probability that a randomly observed value of X will be negative. In a random sample of 20 observed values of X it was found that 17 were negative and 3 were positive. Test the hypothesis that $\theta = 3$ against the alternative hypothesis that $\theta > 3$.

14. The random variable X is distributed with probability density function f, where

$$f(x) = \alpha x^{-(\alpha+1)}, \quad \text{for } x \geq 1,$$
$$f(x) = 0 \quad , \quad \text{otherwise.}$$

To test the hypothesis that $\alpha = 2$ against the alternative hypothesis that $\alpha \neq 2$, it is decided to take a random sample of 100 observations of X and to count the number, R that have values greater than 5. Given that the observed value of R was 9 carry out the test and state your conclusion about the value of α.

3.2.3 Testing the mean of a Poisson distribution

Let $X_1, X_2, ..., X_n$ denote a random sample of n observations from the distribution $Po(\mu)$, where μ is unknown. Suppose that the sample observations are to be used to test the hypothesis that $\mu = \mu_0$. We know that $Y = \Sigma X_i$ has the distribution $Po(n\mu)$ and mean $n\mu$. Thus, if H_0 is true the expected value of Y is $n\mu_0$. It follows that the test can be done by comparing the observed value y of Y with $n\mu_0$.

CASE A : $H_0 : \mu = \mu_0$ against $H_1 : \mu > \mu_0$.

Here, an extreme value of Y will be one which is large compared with $n\mu_0$. Hence, given the observed value y of Y

$$\text{the p-value} = P(Y \geq y \text{ when } \mu = \mu_0).$$

CASE B : $H_0 : \mu = \mu_0$ against $H_1 : \mu < \mu_0$.

An extreme value of Y in this case will be one which is small compared with $n\mu_0$, so that

$$\text{the p-value} = P(Y \leq y \text{ when } \mu = \mu_0).$$

CASE C : $H_0 : \mu = \mu_0$ against $H_1 : \mu \neq \mu_0$.

Using the same argument as in the preceding subsection the p-value in this case is obtained as follows :

(a) If $y > n\mu_0$, the p-value $= 2P(Y \geq y \text{ when } \mu = \mu_0)$.

(b) If $y < n\mu_0$, the p-value $= 2P(Y \leq y \text{ when } \mu = \mu_0)$.

Example 1

Daily records over a long period of time showed that the number of vehicles requiring assistance per day along a certain motorway has a Poisson distribution with mean 0.5. It was suggested that the mean would be greater on wet days. Observation on 10 wet days showed that a total of 9 vehicles required assistance. Assuming that a Poisson distribution is an appropriate model for the number of vehicles requiring assistance on a wet day, test whether the sample evidence is strong enough to validate the suggestion.

Solution

Let X denote the number of vehicles that will require assistance on a wet day and let μ denote the mean of X. Then, $X \sim \text{Po}(\mu)$. We need to test

$$H_0 : \mu = 0.5 \text{ against } H_1 : \mu > 0.5$$

Let Y denote the total number of vehicles that will require assistance on 10 wet days. Then, $Y \sim \text{Po}(10\,\mu)$ and if H_0 is true, $Y \sim \text{Po}(5)$.

Since the observed value of Y was $y = 9$,

the p-value $= P(Y \geq 9 \text{ when } H_0 \text{ is true})$.

Referring to Table 2 with $\mu = 5$ (the mean of Y when H_0 is true) we find that

the p-value $= 0.0681$.

As this is slightly > 0.05 the evidence is not strong enough to reject H_0 and, consequently, we are not justified in supporting the suggestion.

Example 2

In the situation described in Example 1 it was found that a total of 40 vehicles required assistance over 55 wet days. Test whether this result is sufficient to justify concluding that the average number of vehicles requiring assistance per wet day is greater than 0.5. Let Y denote the total number of vehicles that require assistance on 55 wet days. Then $Y \sim \text{Po}(55\,\mu)$, where μ is the average number of vehicles requiring assistance per wet day.

Solution

With H_0 and H_1 as in Example 1 it follows that if H_0 is true then $Y \sim \text{Po}(27.5)$.

In this case, since the observed value of Y is $y = 40$,

the p-value $= P(Y \geq 40 \text{ given that } H_0 \text{ is true})$.

Since $\mu = 27.5$ is not covered in Table 2 we shall approximate the distribution of Y by the normal distribution $N(27.5, 27.5)$. On applying the continuity correction and the normal approximation we have

the p-value $= P(Y \geq 39.5$ when H_0 is true)

$$\approx P\left(Z \geq \frac{39.5 - 27.5}{\sqrt{27.5}} \right) \approx P(Z \geq 2.29) \approx 0.011.$$

The sample evidence is now strong enough to reject H_0 and to conclude that the mean number of vehicles requiring assistance on a wet day is greater that 0.5.

Exercise 3.2.3

1. In the past, the number of claims that were made per week to an insurance company had a Poisson distribution with mean 1.25. In a recent four-week period a total of 10 claims were received by the company. Is the company justified in concluding that the mean number of claims per week has increased?

2. A survey of tabloid newspapers showed that the number of mis-spellings per page had a Poisson distribution with mean 1.4. Five pages of a particular tabloid newspaper contained 3 mis-spellings. Test whether the mean number of mis-spellings in this particular tabloid newspaper is less than 1.4.

3. Past records have indicated that the number of accidents along a particular roadway has a Poisson distribution, the average number per month being 10. During a month when additional warning signs had been erected along the roadway the number of accidents that occurred was 5. The Road Safety Officer decided to test whether the signs had been effective in reducing the number of accidents. Having set up appropriate null and alternative hypotheses for the test the Officer calculated the p-value to be approximately 0.07. Show how this p-value was obtained and state what the Officer's conclusion should be.

4. Records over several years showed that the number of car thefts per week in a small town had a Poisson distribution with mean 1.6. In one particular week the town's local newspaper published an article bearing the heading "Car Thefts On The Increase". The article stated that during the past five weeks there had been a total of 14 car thefts in the town. Test the strength of the evidence for the claim made in the heading of the article.

5. Records of absenteeism at a factory showed that the number of absentees per working day had a Poisson distribution with mean 1.2. During a subsequent week of five working days the numbers of absentees were 2, 1, 3, 3, 2, respectively. Test whether the evidence of that week is strong enough to conclude that the mean number of absentees per week has changed.

6. The nature of a radioactive source can be identified from the mean rate of emissions. For a type-A source the mean rate of emissions is known to be 2.4 per minute. Given that there were 3 emissions from an unidentified source over a period of four minutes test whether this evidence is sufficiently strong to justify identifying the source as not being of type-A.

7. The number of radios sold per week by a certain shop has a Poisson distribution with mean 5. In the week following the appointment of an additional sales assistant a total of 7 radios were sold. Test whether the additional appointment has increased the mean number of radios sold per week.

8. Experiments were conducted to determine whether an antibiotic spray is effective in reducing the number of bacterial colonies that will develop in dishes of nutrient exposed to an infected environment. It is known that the number of colonies that will develop per unsprayed dish has a Poisson distribution with mean 7.5.

(a) In an experiment in which one dish of the nutrient was sprayed, the number of colonies that developed was 3. Determine whether this result provides sufficient evidence to conclude that the spray is effective in reducing the mean number of bacterial colonies that develop.

(b) In another experiment, four dishes were sprayed and the numbers of colonies that developed were 3, 5, 6 and 4, respectively. Determine whether these results provide sufficient evidence to justify concluding that the spray is effective.

3.3 Significance testing

Introduction

In Section 3.2 we showed that when testing some null hypothesis H_0, the p-value was a measure of how unlikely it was that H_0 was true. The smaller the p-value the stronger is the sample evidence against H_0. We made the point that it is up to the investigator to decide whether a calculated p-value was acceptably small enough to justify the rejection of H_0. That decision would have to be based on the seriousness of the consequences should H_0 be wrongfully rejected. Ideally, the investigator should be aware of these consequences before the sample is taken and, therefore, be able to give a quantitative value for the probability that he/she is willing to accept of wrongfully rejecting H_0. A pre-specified value for this probability is called the **significance level** and is usually denoted by α. The significance level is often quoted as a percentage. Thus for example, if $\alpha = 0.05$, we say that the test should be such that the significance level is 5%. When a devised test having significance level α is applied to the observed sample the investigator should reject H_0 only if $\alpha \geq$ the p-value. Thus, **the p-value is the lowest significance level for H_0 to be rejected**. It follows that if α has been specified and the sample observations are available it is sufficient to evaluate the p-value and to reject H_0 only if $\alpha \geq$ the p-value.

However, a pre-specified significance level has a role of its own in hypothesis testing. In particular, given α, it is possible, prior to taking the sample, to devise a **decision rule** which is to be applied to the sample so that the probability of the rule wrongfully rejecting H_0 is equal to α. As in Section 3.2, an appropriate statistic T is chosen for the test and the decision rule will then specify the set of values of T for which H_0 should be rejected; that set of values is referred to as the **critical region**. To summarise, we have the following definition:

Definition. A decision rule which is to be applied to a sample is said to have significance level α if the probability of the rule rejecting H_0 when H_0 is true is equal to α.

We shall be considering two problems, namely (a) finding the significance level of a given decision rule, and (b) finding a decision rule which has a specified significance level. The procedures will be demonstrated in the following subsections which deal with the same situations as in Section 3.2.

3.3.1 Significance testing the mean of a normal distribution of known variance

Consider a random variable whose distribution is $N(\mu, \sigma^2)$, where σ is known and it is required to test $H_0 : \mu = \mu_0$ for some specified μ_0. Suppose that the test is to be based on the values in a random sample of n observations of X. As in Section 3.2.1 the obvious choice of test statistic is the sample mean $\overline{X}$ whose distribution is known to be $N(\mu, \sigma^2/n)$.

CASE A : Testing $H_0 : \mu = \mu_0$ against $H_1 : \mu > \mu_0$

In this case it is clear that the decision rule to apply to the sample should be of the form:

Reject H_0 only if $\overline{X} \geq c$ (the critical region)

for some constant c. The significance level of this rule is given by

$$\alpha = P(\text{the decision rule will reject } H_0 \text{ when } H_0 \text{ is true})$$

$$= P(\overline{X} \geq c \text{ given that } \mu = \mu_0) = P\left(Z \geq \frac{c - \mu_0}{SD(\overline{X})}\right) \tag{1}$$

where $Z \sim N(0, 1)$ and $SD(\overline{X}) = \sigma/\sqrt{n}$.

(a) *The significance level of a given decision rule.*

The significance level for a given value of c can be evaluated from the right-hand side of (1) using Table 3.

(b) *The decision rule given α.*

For a decision rule having significance level α the value of c is the solution of (1); that is, c must be such that

$$\frac{c - \mu_0}{SD(\overline{X})} = z_\alpha,$$

where z_α is such that $P(Z \geq z_\alpha) = \alpha$ whose value can be determined from Table 4. Solving for c it follows that the decision rule of significance level α is

Reject H_0 only if $\overline{X} \geq \mu_0 + z_\alpha SD(\overline{X})$.

This is equivalent to rejecting H_0 if

$$z = \frac{\overline{X} - \mu_0}{SD(\overline{X})} \geq z_\alpha \tag{2}$$

which is probably more convenient when applying this type of test.

CASE B : Testing $H_0 : \mu = \mu_0$ against $H_1 : \mu < \mu_0$.

The decision rule in this case will be of the form $\overline{X} \leq c$. Replacing $\geq$ by $\leq$ in the above the equation corresponding to (1) is

$$\alpha = P(\overline{X} \leq c \text{ when } \mu = \mu_0) = P\left(Z \leq \frac{c - \mu_0}{SD(\overline{X})}\right) \tag{3}$$

It follows that

(a) for any given c the significance level of the decision rule is given by the right-hand side of (3).

(b) the decision rule having significance level α is

$$\text{Reject } H_0 \text{ only if } \overline{X} \leq \mu_0 - z_\alpha SD(\overline{X})$$

which is equivalent to rejecting H_0 if

$$z = \frac{\overline{X} - \mu_0}{SD(\overline{X})} \leq -z_\alpha \qquad (4)$$

CASE C : Testing $H_0 : \mu = \mu_0$ against $H_1 : \mu \neq \mu_0$.

With a two-sided alternative hypothesis the decision rule will take the form

$$\text{Reject } H_0 \text{ only if } \overline{X} \geq c_1 \text{ or if } \overline{X} \leq c_2,$$

where c_1 and c_2 are constants. The significance level of this rule is given by

$$\begin{aligned}
\alpha &= P(\overline{X} \geq c_1 \text{ or } \overline{X} \leq c_2 \text{ when } H_0 \text{ is true}) \\
&= P(\overline{X} \geq c_1 \text{ when } \mu = \mu_0) + P(\overline{X} \leq c_2 \text{ when } \mu = \mu_0), \\
&= P\left(Z \geq \frac{c_1 - \mu_0}{SD(\overline{X})}\right) + P\left(Z \leq \frac{c_2 - \mu_0}{SD(\overline{X})}\right)
\end{aligned} \qquad (5)$$

(a) Given the values of c_1 and c_2, the right-hand side of (5) can be evaluated to give the significance level of that decision rule.

(b) For a given α, equation (5) will have a multitude of possible values of c_1 and c_2. The convention is to equate the two probabilities on the right-hand side of (5), in which case c_1 and c_2 will be the solutions of

$$P\left(Z \geq \frac{c_1 - \mu_0}{SD(\overline{X})}\right) = \frac{1}{2}\alpha \quad \text{and} \quad P\left(Z \leq \frac{c_2 - \mu_0}{SD(\overline{X})}\right) = \frac{1}{2}\alpha.$$

Solving these equations the decision rule having significance level α is

$$\text{Reject } H_0 \text{ only if } \overline{X} \geq \mu_0 + z_{1/2\alpha} SD(\overline{X}) \text{ or } \overline{X} \leq \mu_0 - z_{1/2\alpha} SD(\overline{X})$$

which is equivalent to rejecting H_0 if

$$z = \frac{\overline{X} - \mu_0}{SD(\overline{X})} \geq z_{\alpha/2} \quad \text{or} \quad z = \frac{\overline{X} - \mu_0}{SD(\overline{X})} \leq -z_{\alpha/2} \qquad (6)$$

Example 1

A particular brand of electric light bulbs have lifetimes that are normally distributed with mean 1200 hours and standard deviation 150 hours. It is suspected that a particular batch is substandard. To test this suspicion a random sample of 50 bulbs is to be taken from the batch and their lifetimes are to be measured.

(a) Determine the significance level of the decision rule which will conclude that the batch is substandard if the sample mean lifetime is less than 1160 hours.

(b) Determine the decision rule which will have a significance level of 1%.

(c) What conclusion should be drawn if the observed sample mean is 1150 hours and the chosen significance level is 1%?

Solution

Let μ hours be the mean lifetime of the bulbs in the suspected batch. The appropriate null and alternative hypotheses are

$$H_0 : \mu = 1200 \quad \text{and} \quad H_1 : \mu < 1200.$$

Let $\overline{X}$ denote the mean lifetime of the 50 sampled bulbs. We know that the distribution of $\overline{X}$ is normal with mean μ and standard deviation

$$SD(\overline{X}) = 150/\sqrt{50} \approx 21.2132.$$

(a) The significance level of the rule which rejects H_0 if $\overline{X} < 1160$ is

$$\alpha = P(\overline{X} < 1160 \text{ when } \mu = 1200) = P\left(Z < \frac{1160 - 1200}{21.2132}\right) = P(Z < -1.89) = 0.0294$$

(b) Consider the decision rule which will reject H_0 if $\overline{X} \leq c$. We need to find c so that the significance level is 0.01. That is, c must be such that

$$P(\overline{X} \leq c \text{ when } \mu = 1200) = 0.01$$

or, equivalently, such that

$$P\left(Z \leq \frac{c - 1200}{21.2132}\right) = 0.01.$$

From Table 4 we find that the value of z for which $P(Z \leq z) = 0.01$ is -2.326. Hence,

$$\frac{c - 1200}{21.2132} = -2.326 \quad \text{and} \quad c \approx 1150.66$$

Thus, the decision rule of significance level 0.01 is

Reject H_0 if the sample mean is ≤ 1150.66.

(c) Since the observed sample mean of 1150 is < 1150.66, H_0 should be rejected and the batch deemed to be substandard.

[Alternatively, it may be shown that the p-value = 0.009. Since the chosen significance level of 0.01 is greater than the p-value, the null hypothesis should be rejected].

Example 2

The amounts of milk delivered into cartons by a machine are normally distributed with standard deviation 8·3 ml. The machine is set so that the mean delivery per carton is 500ml. As part of the quality control process samples of 50 cartons are taken periodically to check that the mean amount delivered is 500 ml. One such sample was such that the mean of the deliveries was 502·5 ml. Test, using a significance level of 5%, whether the machine needs adjusting.

Solution

Let μ ml denote the mean amount delivered by the machine when the sample is taken. Since it is not possible, prior to sampling, to decide whether the machine is operating properly, under-delivering or over-delivering, the appropriate null and alternative hypotheses are:

$$H_0: \mu = 500 \text{ and } H_1: \mu \neq 500 .$$

For a sample of size 50 the sampling distribution of the sample mean when H_0 is true is normal with mean 500 and standard deviation $8 \cdot 3/\sqrt{50}$. That is,

$$\overline{X} \sim N(500, \frac{8 \cdot 3^2}{50})$$

or, equivalently,

$$Z = \frac{\overline{X} - 500}{8 \cdot 3/\sqrt{50}} \sim N(0,1).$$

The observed value of Z is

$$z = \frac{502 \cdot 5 - 500}{8 \cdot 3/\sqrt{50}} = 2 \cdot 13 .$$

With a significance level of $0 \cdot 05$ and a two-sided H_1 the critical value of z is $z_{0.025} = 1 \cdot 96$ (from Table 4). Since the observed value of z is $> 1 \cdot 96$ we reject the null hypothesis and conclude that the machine needs to be adjusted. Furthermore, since $\overline{x} > 500$ we can conclude that the machine is over-delivering.

[Alternatively, it is left as an exercise to show that the p-value for the observed sample is equal to $0 \cdot 041$. Since this is less than the stipulated significance level of $0 \cdot 05$ the null hypothesis should be rejected and the conclusion is as given above.]

Exercise 3.3.1

1. The weekly takings (£) of a grocery shop before modernisation were normally distributed with mean 1243 and standard deviation 105. The takings in nine weeks after the modernisation had been completed were :

    1263, 1306, 1178, 1175, 1309, 1263, 1418, 1387, 1339

    Using a 10% significance level and assuming that the standard deviation is unchanged, carry out a test to decide if the mean weekly takings has increased.

2. The breaking strengths of a particular brand of thread are known to be normally distributed with mean μ and standard deviation 1.4. A random sample of 36 newly produced pieces of thread are found to have a mean breaking strength of 9.3 units. Test, at the 5% significance level, the null hypothesis that $\mu = 9.7$ against the alternative that $\mu < 9.7$.

3. The times of a 100-metre sprinter during last season were normally distributed with mean 10.7 seconds and standard deviation 0.15 seconds. In an attempt to improve the standard of his performance he gets a new coach on a temporary basis before the start of the new season. The sprinter decides to assess whether the new coach has been beneficial after the first four races of the new season. Assume that the new season's times are still normally distributed with unchanged standard deviation.

(a) Find the significance level of the rule that concludes that the new coach has been beneficial if the sprinter's mean time in the first four races is less than 10.58 seconds.

(b) Given that the sprinter's mean time in the first four races was 10.6 seconds carry out a test at the 10% significance level to see if the change of coach has been beneficial.

4. A nautical chart shows that the depths of a sea bed in a certain area are normally distributed with mean 1515 fathoms and standard deviation 65 fathoms. A survey vessel measured the depths of the sea bed at 25 randomly chosen locations and found that the mean depth at these locations was 1546 fathoms. Using a 1% significance level determine whether the sample results cast doubt on the accuracy of the chart.

5. A lathe is adjusted to produce parts whose diameters are normally distributed with mean 10 cm, and standard deviation 0.12 cm. A check is to be made that the mean diameter is still 10 cm by taking a random sample of 15 parts and measuring their diameters.

(a) Find the significance level of the decision rule that will conclude that the mean diameter is different from 10 cm if the sample mean diameter is greater than 10.02 cm or less than 9.98 cm.

(b) Find the decision rule that should be applied if its significance level is to be 5%.

(c) What is the conclusion using the rule in (b) if the sample mean diameter is 9.93 cm?

3.3.2 Significance testing a probability

Let X denote the number of successes in n independent trials of a random experiment in each of which the probability of a success is θ. The observed value of X is to be used to test the null hypothesis $H_0 : \theta = \theta_0$.

Example 1

The manufacturer of a new type of seeding compost claims that seeds sown in this new compost will have a higher germination rate than if they were sown in ordinary compost. For a particular variety of seed sown in ordinary compost the germination rate is known to be 0.7. To test the manufacturer's claim an experiment was conducted in which 20 of the seeds were sown in the new compost and the number, X, that germinated was counted.

(a) Find the significance level of the decision rule that accepts the claim if $X \geq 17$.

(b) Find a decision rule whose significance level is 0.05. What conclusion should be drawn if 18 of the seeds germinated?

Solution

We know that $X \sim B(20, \theta)$ and we want to test

$$H_0 : \theta = 0.7 \text{ against } H_1 : \theta > 0.7.$$

(a) The significance level of the rule which rejects H_0 if $X \geq 17$ is $P(X \geq 17 \text{ when } \theta = 0.7)$. Since 0.7 is not included in Table 1, let X' denote the number of seeds that do not germinate. Then assuming that H_0 is true, $X' \sim B(20, 0.3)$ and

$$P(X \geq 17 \text{ when } \theta = 0.7) = P(X' \leq 3) = 0.1071 \text{ from Table 1,}$$

which is the required significance level.

(b) Consider the decision rule which rejects H_0 if $X \geq c$, where c is such that the significance level is 0.05. That is, $P(X \geq c \text{ when } H_0 \text{ is true}) = 0.05$. With X' as defined in (a) we need to find c such that $P(X' \leq 20 - c) = 0.05$.

Referring to Table 1 we find that

$$P(X' \leq 2) = 0.0355 \text{ and } P(X' \leq 3) = 0.1071.$$

It follows that there is no decision rule whose significance level is exactly 0.05. A sensible criterion to use in such a case is to choose a decision rule whose significance level is as close as possible to 0.05 and preferably less than 0.05 (so as to give more protection against wrongfully rejecting H_0). Thus, the decision rule recommended here is to accept the claim as being true only if $X \geq 18$, whose significance level is 0.0355.

[The problem that has arisen here will occur generally when dealing with a discrete random variable.]

Given that the observed value of X was 18, which is in the critical region of the above decision rule, the conclusion is to accept the manufacturer's claim as being true.

[If (b) had merely asked for the conclusion if 18 of the seeds had germinated assuming a significance level of 0.05, then the answer is more readily obtained by finding the p-value, which is $P(X \geq 18 \text{ when } H_0 \text{ is true}) = 0.0355$. Since 0.05 is > the p-value the conclusion is to accept the claim. This advantage of the p-value is generally true, and particularly so when the test statistic is discrete.]

Example 2

A coin is to be tossed 50 times to test whether it is unbiased.

(a) Find the significance level of the decision rule:

 Conclude that the coin is biased if $X \leq 19$ or if $X \geq 31$,

 where X is the number of heads obtained.

(b) Using a 5% significance level what conclusion should be drawn if 32 heads are obtained?

Solution

(a) Let θ be the probability of tossing a head. Then $X \sim B(50, \theta)$ and we wish to test

 $H_0 : \theta = 0.5$ against $H_1 : \theta \neq 0.5$.

The significance level of the given decision rule is

 $P(X \leq 19 \text{ when } \theta = 0.5) + P(X \geq 31 \text{ when } \theta = 0.5)$

From Table 1 with $n = 50$ and $p = 0.5$ we find that

 $P(X \leq 19) = 0.0595$ and $P(X \geq 31) = 0.0595$.

Hence the significance level of the rule is $2 \times 0.0595 = 0.119$.

(b) Since the observed value of X is 32, which is greater than the expected value (25) of X when H_0 is true, and H_1 is two-sided we have

the p-value $= 2P(X \geq 32 \text{ when } \theta = 0.5) = 2 \times 0.0325 = 0.065$.

Since the specified significance level of 0.05 is less than the p-value there is insufficient evidence at the 5% significance level to justify rejecting the unbiasedness of the coin.

Use of a normal approximation

Example 3

In a certain constituency 40% of the electorate voted Labour in the last general election. An opinion poll is to be conducted in the constituency to test whether or not there has been a change in the level of support for the Labour party since the last election. In the poll of 600 persons it was found that 215 intended to vote Labour in the next election. What conclusion should be drawn if the significance level is 5%?

Solution

Let θ denote the proportion of voters who intend to vote Labour. Since the poll is intended to detect whether the proportion has changed from 0.4, the appropriate null and alternative hypotheses are $H_0 : \theta = 0.4$ and $H_1 : \theta \neq 0.4$. Let X denote the number of the 600 persons to be sampled who intend to vote Labour. Then $X \sim B(600, \theta)$.

Since the observed value of X was 215, which is less than 240 (the expected value of X when $\theta = 0.4$), and H_1 is two-sided

the p-value $= 2P(X \le 215$ when $\theta = 0.4)$.

Since n = 600 is very large we can approximate the distribution B(600, 0.4) by a normal distribution having mean $600 \times 0.4 = 240$ and variance $240 \times 0.6 = 144$. Using this approximation and applying the correction for continuity we have :

$$\text{the p-value} = 2P(X < 215.5 \text{ when } \theta = 0.4) \approx 2P\left(Z > \frac{215.5 - 240}{\sqrt{144}}\right)$$

$$\approx 2P(Z < -2.04) \approx 2 \times 0.0207 = 0.0414.$$

Since the specified significance level of 0.05 is greater than the p-value we reject the null hypothesis and conclude that the proportion of voters supporting Labour has dropped since the last election.

Exercise 3.3.2

1. A firm which produces cardigans has found that when a particular machine is operating properly 5% of the cardigans it produces are flawed. An inspection scheme requires 10 cardigans to be selected at random and examined for flaws. The machine is deemed to require adjustment if at least two of the cardigans in the sample are flawed. Find the significance level of this decision rule.

2. The manufacturer of the dog food "Woof" advertised on television that more than 7 dogs out of 10 preferred "Woof" to any other brand of dog food. To test this claim each of 20 dogs was presented with a free choice from a wide selection of brands of dog food including "Woof". The claim is to be accepted as being valid if at least 18 of the dogs opt for "Woof". Find the significance level of this decision rule.

3. A certain drug is known to cure 65% of patients treated. A pharmaceutical company has developed a new drug which is claimed to have a higher cure rate. To test the claim the new drug is to be trialled on 50 patients.

(a) Set up appropriate null and alternative hypotheses.

(b) A doctor decided that he would use the new drug if at least 36 of the 50 patients given the new drug were cured. Find the significance level.

(c) Derive a decision rule to use whose significance level is as close as possible to 0.05 without exceeding it. State the conclusion to be drawn if 40 of the 50 patients given the new drug are cured.

4. A coin is suspected to be such that when tossed a head is more likely than a tail. To test this suspicion the coin is to be tossed 50 times and a conclusion is to be drawn on the basis of the number, X, of heads that are tossed. Construct such a test having significance level as close to 0.05 as is possible. State the actual significance level of your test.

5. A hospital's records showed that 3 out of every 10 casualty patients who reported to the hospital had to wait longer than 20 minutes before being seen by a doctor. The hospital decided to have an additional doctor available in the casualty department, after which it was found that of the next 20 casualties only two had to wait more than 20 minutes before being seen by a doctor. Test whether the extra doctor has decreased the number of casualties having to wait more than 20 minutes, using a significance level of (a) 2%, (b) 5%.

6. A coin is to be tossed 20 times to test if it is unbiased. Let X denote the number of heads that will be obtained.

(a) Find the significance level of the decision rule which will reject H_0 if $X \geq 15$ or if $X \leq 5$.

(b) Given that 6 heads were tossed determine whether it should be concluded that the coin is biased if the significance level is 10%.

7. It has been claimed that 10% of the pupils at a large school have part-time jobs. The headmaster is of the opinion that the proportion is greater than 10%. In a random sample of 100 pupils from the school it was found that 15 of them had part-time jobs. Assuming a 5% significance level is the sample evidence sufficiently strong to support the headmaster's opinion?

8. A gambler claims that he can throw a fair die in such a way that his probability of getting a 6 is greater than 1/6. To justify his claim he throws the die 50 times. Given that a 6 occurred in 13 of the throws test his claim using a 5% significance level.

9. A manufacturer of colour televisions claims that more than 90% of the sets will be trouble-free for at least two years. In a random sample of 100 such sets that had been sold it was found that 5 of them needed attention during the first two years. Assuming a 5% significance level should the manufacturer's claim be rejected?

10. A large college claims that it admits equal numbers of males and females. A random sample of 400 students at the college was found to consist of 210 males and 190 females. Test the claim using a 5% significance level.

11. In 100 tosses of a coin a head occurred 61 times. Use a 5% significance level to test whether the coin is unbiased.

3.3.3 Significance testing a Poisson mean

A random sample of n observations is to be taken from a Poisson distribution having unknown mean μ in order to test $H_0 : \mu = \mu_0$. As in Section 3.2.3, an appropriate test statistic here is Y = the sum of the n values in the sample since, when H_0 is true, $Y \sim Po(n\mu_0)$.

Example 1

The random variable X has the Poisson distribution with unknown mean μ. A random sample of three observations of X is to be taken in order to test $H_0 : \mu = 1.7$ against $H_1 : \mu < 1.7$.

(a) It is decided to reject H_0 if the sum of the three values obtained is less than 3.

(i) Find the significance level of this decision rule.

(ii) Find the probability that this decision rule will not reject H_0 when the true value of μ is 1.2.

(b) Find a decision rule having a significance level as close as possible to 0.05. State the actual significance level of the rule.

Solution

(a) Let Y denote the sum of the values of the three observations of X. Then $Y \sim Po(3\mu)$.

(i) The significance level of the decision rule which rejects H_0 if Y is < 3 is

$$P(Y < 3 \text{ when } \mu = 1.7) = P(Y \le 2 \text{ when } \mu = 1.7).$$

When $\mu = 1.7$, $Y \sim Po(5.1)$. Since Table 2 does not include this distribution we shall use the Poisson formula to evaluate the significance level, which in this case is

$$P(Y = y) = e^{-5.1} \times \frac{5.1^y}{y!} \quad , \quad y = 0, 1, 2, 3, \ldots$$

Hence the significance level is

$$P(Y \le 2) = P(Y = 0) + P(Y = 1) + P(Y = 2)$$
$$= e^{-5.1}(1 + 5.1 + 5.1^2/2) = 0.1165.$$

(ii) If $\mu = 1.2$, then $Y \sim Po(3.6)$, and the probability that the decision rule will not reject H_0 is $P(Y \ge 3) = 0.6973$ from Table 2.

(b) Consider the decision rule : Reject H_0 if $Y \le c$, where c is to be such that

$$P(Y \le 2 \text{ when } \mu = 1.7) \approx 0.05.$$

When $\mu = 1.7$ the distribution of Y is Po(5.1). From (a)(i) above we have $P(Y \le 2) = 0.1165$, which is greater than 0.05.

$$P(Y \le 1) = P(Y = 0) + P(Y = 1) = e^{-5.1}(1 + 5.1) = 0.0372.$$

Hence, the decision rule having significance level as close as possible to 0.05 is:

Reject H_0 if the sum of the sample values is ≤ 1 (the critical region).

The actual significance level of this rule is 0.0372.

Example 2

The number of parking tickets issued per weekday by the traffic wardens in a town has a Poisson distribution with mean 1.4. The town council decides to employ one more warden on a temporary basis to see if the number of tickets issued will be increased on average. Let X denote the number of tickets issued during the first five weekdays after the employment of the additional warden.

(a) The council decided to conclude that the average number of tickets issued per week had increased if the observed value of X was 10 or more. Find the significance level of this decision rule.

(b) Given that the observed value of X was 11 find the p-value, and deduce the minimum significance level for the conclusion to be that the mean number of tickets issued per weekday has increased.

Solution

(a) Let μ denote the mean number of tickets issued per weekday after the employment of the additional warden. We want to test $H_0 : \mu = 1.4$ against $H_1 : \mu > 1.4$. Assuming that the Poisson distribution is still appropriate the distribution of X is $Po(5\mu)$.

The significance level of the rule "Reject H_0 if $X \geq 10$" is $P(X \geq 10$ when $\mu = 1.4)$. Referring to Table 2 for the Poisson distribution with mean $5 \times 1.4 = 7$, the significance level is 0.1685.

(b) Given that $X = 11$, the p-value is

$$P(X \geq 11 \text{ when } \mu = 1.4) = 0.0985,$$

on using Table 2 for a Poisson distribution with mean 7.

Hence, the minimum significance level for H_0 to be rejected is 0.0985, or just under 10%.

Example 3

Manufactured cloth is passed for sale if the average number of flaws per metre of the cloth is less than 0.5. A decision on whether or not to pass a roll of the cloth is based on the observed number of flaws in a length of 100 m from the roll. Denoting this number by X, construct a decision rule having a significance level of approximately 0.01. It may be assumed that the number of flaws has a Poisson distribution.

Solution

Let μ denote the mean number of flaws per metre of the cloth. The appropriate null and alternative hypotheses in this case are $H_0 : \mu = 0.5$ and $H_1 : \mu < 0.5$. Since X is the number of flaws in 100 metres the distribution of X is $Po(100\mu)$. In particular, if H_0 is true, then X has the distribution $Po(50)$. In view of H_1, the decision rule has to be of the form

Reject H_0 only if $X \le c$,

where c is a positive integer. We need to find a positive integer c so that the significance level is approximately 0.01.

Since Table 2 does not include the Poisson distribution with mean 50 we shall use the normal approximation having mean and variance equal to 50. Thus, on applying the continuity correction we need to solve

$$P(X \le c) \equiv P(X < c + 0.5) \approx P\left(Z < \frac{c + 0.5 - 50}{\sqrt{50}}\right) \approx 0.01$$

Referring to Table 4 we find that the solution to this equation is
$$\frac{c + 0.5 - 50}{\sqrt{50}} \approx -2.326.$$

Hence, $c \approx 50 - 0.5 - 2.326\sqrt{50} \approx 33.053.$

We now round down to the nearest integer and take $c = 33$. Rounding down is advisable here in order to ensure that the significance level (the probability of wrongfully rejecting H_0) is less than stipulated. Thus, the decision rule should be : Pass the roll only if X is ≤ 33.

Exercise 3.3.3

1. The number of flaws in a given length of cloth has a Poisson distribution. The manufacturer claims that the mean number of flaws per metre is 0.2. To test this claim against the alternative that the mean number of flaws per metre is greater than 0.2, it is decided to examine a length 10 cm of the cloth and to reject the claim if it contains 6 or more flaws. Find the significance level of this test. Also find the number that should replace the 6 above so that the new rule will have a significance level of approximately 0.05.

2. The number of times that a computer needs attention has a Poisson distribution, the mean number per month being 4.25. During the first month after the computer had undergone a major overhaul there was only one occasion when it needed attention. Using a 5% significance level determine whether it is justifiable to conclude that the

major overhaul has reduced the mean number of times that the computer needs attention.

3. The number of emergency calls per hour to a gas board over a weekend has a Poisson distribution with mean 0.7. It was suggested that the mean would be greater than 0.7 over a very cold weekend. During a very cold weekend in the winter the office received 11 emergency calls during the first 10 hours. Show that, with a significance level of 5%, this does not provide sufficient evidence to justify concluding that the mean number of calls over that weekend is greater than 0.7. Write down the smallest significance level that would justify the conclusion.

4. An employer is seeking a typist who can be relied upon not to mistype more than one character per page on average. An applicant for the position was given four pages to type and it was found that she had mistyped a total of seven characters. Use a 10% significance level to test the hypothesis that her average number of mistyped characters per page is 1 against the alternative that it is greater than 1. Assume that the number of mistyped characters per page has a Poisson distribution.

5. It is required to test $H_0 : \mu = 2$ against $H_1 : \mu \neq 2$, where μ is the mean of a Poisson distribution. The test is to be based on a random sample of five observations from the distribution.

(a) Find the significance level of the decision rule which rejects H_0 if the sample mean is < 0.4 or is > 3.4.

(b) Assuming that the chosen significance level is 0.06, what conclusion should be drawn if the sample mean was 0.8?

6. The random variable X has the Poisson distribution with mean μ. A random sample of 23 observations had a sum equal to 30. Use a 5% significance level to test $H_0 : \mu = 1.7$ against $H_1 : \mu < 1.7$.

7. The counts of bacterial colonies that developed in 10 exposed Petri dishes were :

$$12, 13, 8, 17, 16, 8, 18, 15, 9, 11$$

Test, at the 1% significance level, that the mean number of bacterial colonies that will develop per Petri dish under the same exposure is equal to 10, against the alternative that it is greater than 10.

8. It has been claimed that the mean number of impurities per sheet of glass from a certain manufacturer is 2.5. Test this claim, using a significance level of 5%, given that the total number of impurities in 100 sheets of glass was 278. Assume that the number of impurities per sheet of glass has a Poisson distribution.

9. The number of cars arriving at a road junction in 45 consecutive five-minute periods were as follows :

Number of cars arriving	0	1	2	3	4	5
Number of time periods	6	13	11	9	3	3

    Assuming that the number of cars arriving in a five-minute period has a Poisson distribution, test, at the 1% level of significance, the hypothesis that the mean of the distribution is equal to 1.5 against the alternative that it is not equal to 1.5.

10. Over a long period of time the number of occasions that a piece of equipment has had to be repaired by a technician has averaged 1.9 times per month. A new technician was employed to be solely responsible for the maintenance of this equipment. It may be assumed that the number of times per month that this technician will be required to repair the equipment has a Poisson distribution. In each of the following cases use a 5% significance level to test whether the mean number of repairs per month is different from 1.9.

(a) In the new technician's first three months he was required to repair the equipment twice.

(b) In the new technician's first 30 months he was required to repair the equipment a total of 43 times.

Miscellaneous Questions on Chapter 3

1. The brand of engine oil used by a racing motorist has a viscosity of 145 units. In order to test whether a new brand differs in viscosity he decides to measure the viscosity of 12 samples of the new oil. It may be assumed that the apparatus used gives readings which are normally distributed with mean equal to the true viscosity and standard deviation 6 units. The readings obtained were :

    139, 152, 143, 154, 145, 153, 147, 146, 161, 147, 148, 149.

    Let μ denote the true viscosity of the new oil. Find the p-value when testing $H_0 : \mu = 145$ against $H_1 : \mu > 145$. Hence, state the conclusion that should be drawn if the specified significance level is 0.05.

2. Cans of orange drink are filled by a machine which delivers a quantity of the drink which is normally distributed with a standard deviation of 6 ml. The manufacturer does not wish to give short measures and neither does he wish to overfill the cans. The machine has been set to deliver an average of 335 ml per can. In a random

sample of 15 cans it was found that the mean content was 338.6 ml. Test, at the 5% significance level, whether the mean amount delivered is different from 335 ml.

3. The tar yields in cigarettes of a particular brand are known to be normally distributed with standard deviation 0.7. The tar yields (in mg) of a random sample of 10 cigarettes of that brand were : 17.1, 19.2, 18.3, 18.2, 18.9, 17.8, 18.5, 18.3, 16.9, 17.8. Use a 5% significance level to test the hypothesis that the mean tar yield per cigarette is 17.6 mg against the alternative that it is greater than 17.6 mg.

4. A scientist knows that a piece of apparatus which she uses for determining the weight of impurity in a chemical gives readings that are normally distributed with mean equal to the true weight and standard deviation 2.6 mg. She takes 16 samples of 100 g each from a certain batch of chemical and measures the weight of impurity in each. She calculated the sample mean weight to be 6.836 mg. Test whether the true amount of impurity per 100 g of the batch could be 8.0 mg, using a significance level of 5%.

5. The probability that a seed of a particular variety will germinate is p (unknown). Let X denote the number of 20 such seeds that will germinate. It is required to test the null hypothesis that $p = 0.6$. Find the integer r such that the decision rule which rejects the null hypothesis if $X \leq 12 - r$ or if $X \geq 12 + r$ has a significance level of approximately 0.01.

6. Cliff claims that when he tosses a coin he has a better than even chance of calling the outcome correctly. His claim is challenged by Alice and Bill. Alice asks Cliff to toss a coin 20 times and she agrees to accept Cliff's claim if he correctly calls at least 14 of the outcomes. Bill asks Cliff to toss the coin 50 times and agrees to accept Cliff's claim if he correctly calls at least 31 of the outcomes. Show that the significance levels of the decision rules used by Alice and Bill are equal, correct to two decimal places. Determine which of the two decision rules is the more likely to accept Cliff's claim when in fact Cliff's probability of a correct call is 0.7.

7. A factory produces sweets in a variety of colours. A machine selects sweets at random and packs them in boxes of 20. In a random sample of 100 boxes the number of black sweets per box were as given in the following table.

Number of black sweets	0	1	2	3	4	5
Number of boxes	11	29	27	22	7	4

Calculate the proportion of the 2000 sweets sampled that were black

Let θ denote the actual proportion of the sweets produced that are black. Find the p-value of the above data when testing H_0: $\theta = 0.09$ against H_1: $\theta \neq 0.09$. State the conclusion to be drawn if the significance level is 0.05.

8. In one of the states of America the roulette wheels permitted in casinos have 38 divisions, two of which are labelled "0" and result in a win for the casino. A casino is required by law to carry out regular tests on its roulette wheels to ensure that the probability of a "0" does not exceed 1/19. The test procedure consists of spinning a wheel 380 times and recording the number of times a "0" occurred. In one such test a "0" was obtained 27 times. Assuming a 1% significance level, determine whether this particular wheel complies with the legal requirement.

9. The number of emissions per minute from a radioactive source has a Poisson distribution. Let μ denote the mean number per minute from a particular source. It is required to test the null hypothesis H_0: $\mu = 2$ against the alternative hypothesis H_1:$\mu>2$.

(a) One possible test is to count the number X of emissions from the source in a period of 1 minute. Write down the form of decision rule that is appropriate in this case. Derive the decision rule having a significance level as close to 0.05 as possible and write down its actual significance level.

(b) A second possible test is to count the number Y of emissions from the source in a period of 2 minutes. Derive the decision rule (in terms of Y) having a significance level as close as possible to 0.05.

10. The data given in the following table are the observed monthly counts of stillbirths in a county over a period of 132 months.

Number of stillbirths	0	1	2	3	4	5	6	7	8
Number of months	7	18	33	32	20	11	3	6	2

Assuming that the number of stillbirths per month has a Poisson distribution, test the hypothesis that the mean number per month is 2·8 against the alternatives that it is greater than 2·8.

11. (S2 1996) A darts player claims that he can hit the "bull" with 40% of his throws. To test this claim, the darts player participates in a controlled experiment in which he throws a dart 250 times. He hits the "bull" 92 times.

(a) Set up a statistical model of this situation and state appropriate null and alternative hypotheses. [2]

(b) Calculate the p-value of the result obtained in the experiment. Interpret this value in the context of the problem. [5]

12. (S2 1996) In an automatic bottling process, the number of unsatisfactory bottles produced per hour can be modelled by a Poisson distribution with mean μ. When the process is working normally, the value of μ is 4. In order to ensure that μ has not increased, regular checks are carried out in which the number of unsatisfactory bottles, X, produced in a particular hour is determined. If $X \geq 7$, the process is stopped for maintenance.

(a) Write down the appropriate null and alternative hypotheses and find the significance level of the checking procedure. [3]

(b) Find the probability that the checking procedure fails to detect that μ has increased when, in fact, $\mu = 7$. [2]

(c) The company statistician suggests that it might be better to determine the number of unsatisfactory bottles, Y, produced in a 2-hour period. The process would be stopped for maintenance if $Y \geq K$, where K is a positive integer chosen to give a significance level as close to 10% as possible.

(i) Find the value of K.

(ii) Find the probability that this new checking procedure fails to detect that μ has increased when, in fact, $\mu = 7$.

(iii) State, with a reason, whether you think this new checking procedure is better than the old one. [5]

13. (A3 1996) When a scientist measures the concentration of a solution, the reading obtained can be modelled by a normally distributed random variable with mean μ units, equal to the true concentration, and standard deviation 1·6 units.

He is given a solution to analyse, which a colleague believes has a concentration of more than 25 units. He makes four independent measurements of the concentration of the solution, obtaining the following results: 25·1, 27·8, 26·9, 25·8

(a) State appropriate null and alternative hypotheses for a test to determine whether there is sufficient evidence to support the colleague's belief . [1]

(b) Calculate the sample mean $\bar{x}$. [1]

(c) Calculate the p-value of $\bar{x}$ and interpret it in the context of this problem. [5]

14. (A3 1997) David claims to be able to throw a fair die in such a way that the probability of a "6" occurring exceeds $\frac{1}{6}$. In order to test his claim, he decides to throw the die 200 times and to record the number of times a "6" occurs.

(a) Set up a probability model of this situation and state appropriate null and alternative hypotheses. [2]

(b) He obtains a "6" in 40 of the 200 throws.

  (i) Calculate, approximately, the p-value of this result.

  (ii) State the conclusion that should be drawn if the significance level is set at 10%. [5]

15. (S2 1997) Let p denote the probability that a drawing pin thrown onto a table will come to rest with its point upright. A mathematician studied the physical dimensions of the drawing pin and claimed that p was equal to 0·4. To test this claim the drawing pin is to be thrown onto a table 20 times. It is decided to reject the claim if $X \leq 3$ or $X \geq 12$, where X is the number of times that the drawing pin comes to rest with its point upright.

(a) Find the significance level of this decision rule. [3]

(b) Explain what the term "significance level" means in the context of this question. [1]

16. (S2 1997) Over a long period of time the number of accidents in a factory has averaged 1·5 per month. Additional safety devices were installed for a trial period of 6 months in the hope that they would reduce the accident rate. During the trial period there were 3 accidents. The factory manager consulted a statistician for advice as to whether or not the additional safety devices would lead to a reduction in the accident rate. The statistician assumed that a Poisson distribution was appropriate. Based on the information provided the statistician calculated the p-value to be 0·0212.

(a) Write down the null and alternative hypotheses which are appropriate here. [1]

(b) Show how the p-value was calculated. [2]

(c) State, giving a reason for your choice, which of the following recommendations you would report to the factory manager.

  (i) the additional safety devices will almost certainly lead to a reduction in the accident rate,

(ii) the additional safety devices are unlikely to reduce the accident rate,

(iii) the evidence so far is inconclusive, so the safety devices should remain in place for a further period before reaching a conclusion. [1]

17. (A3 1998) During the first half of a season the mean number of goals scored per match by a hockey team was 2·2. The manager introduced new training methods for the second half of the season and she wishes to determine whether the mean number of goals scored per match would increase as a result. She decides to assume that, independently for each match in the second half of the season, the number of goals scored per match can be modelled by a Poisson distribution with mean μ. In the first five matches of the second half of the season the team scored a total of 19 goals.

(i) Determine the p-value of this result when testing the null hypothesis $\mu = 2·2$ against the alternative hypothesis $\mu > 2·2$.

(ii) What conclusion would you reach regarding the value of μ using a 1% significance level?

(iii) State one reason why the proposed model might not accurately describe the situation. [5]

18. (S21998) When a process is operating properly the proportion of defective items produced is equal to 0·01. Periodical inspections are made to check that the proportion of defective items being produced has not increased. Each such inspection consists of taking a random sample of items from the production line and counting the number, X, of defective items in the sample. The decision rule used is to stop the process for investigation if X is 3 or more.

(a) Set up appropriate null and alternative hypotheses for this situation. [1]

(b) Determine the significance level of the decision rule used. [2]

(c) Calculate the probability that an inspection will not lead to the process being stopped even though the proportion of defective items being produced has increased to 0·02. [2]

(d) State one inadequacy of the decision rule used. [1]

19. (S2 1998) The number of late night calls to a particular surgery may be modelled by a Poisson distribution. A check of the records over the past few months showed that the mean number of calls per night had been 2. It is suspected that the mean has increased. To test this suspicion it was decided to monitor the situation every night. In

each of the following cases determine the p-value, or an approximation to it, when testing whether the mean has increased and state your conclusion.

(a) A total of 15 calls were received over 5 nights. [4]

(b) A total of 101 calls were received over 40 nights. [5]

20. (A3 1999) Independently for each page, the number of errors per page made by a student typist can be modelled by a Poisson distribution with mean μ. The typist claims that $\mu = 1\cdot5$ but his tutor suggests that $\mu > 1\cdot5$. They therefore set up the hypotheses H_0: $\mu = 1\cdot5$ versus H_1: $\mu > 1\cdot5$
and the typist agrees to undergo a test in which he types a specified number of pages.

(a) Initially, he types 10 pages and makes a total of 22 errors. Calculate and interpret the p-value of this result. [4]

(b) In view of this result, he is asked to undergo a further test in which he types 50 pages. He makes a total of 93 errors in this test. Using a normal approximation, calculate and interpret the p-value of this result. [6]

21. (S2 1999) The amount of hot water delivered per cup by a vending machine is normally distributed with standard deviation 5 ml. When operating properly the mean amount delivered per cup is 250 ml. Periodical checks are made on the machine, each check consisting of measuring the amounts of hot water delivered to 25 cups. It is decided that the machine should be overhauled if the sample mean delivery per cup is less than 248 ml or greater than 252 ml.

(a) Set up null and alternative hypotheses which are appropriate for such a check. [1]

(b) Determine the significance level of the rule used to decide whether or not to overhaul the machine. [5]

22. (S2 1999) The number of serious road accidents per year in a particular county may be modelled by a Poisson distribution. Records show that the mean number of serious road accidents per year in the county was 15. In an attempt to reduce the number of serious road accidents the county introduced additional speed limits.

(a) In the year following the introduction of the additional speed limits there were 11 serious road accidents in the county. Determine the p-value when testing whether the accident rate has been reduced. State, with a reason, the conclusion you draw from the p-value. [4]

(b) In the three years following the introduction of the additional speed limits a total of 28 serious road accidents occurred in the county. Determine an approximation to the p-value when testing whether the accident rate has been reduced. State, with a reason, the conclusion you draw from this p-value. [7]

NUMERICAL ANSWERS

Exercise 1.1

1. (a) $\frac{1}{64}$ (b) $\frac{81}{256}$ (c) $\frac{1}{4}$ (d) $\frac{95}{176}$ **2.** $133\frac{1}{3}$, $\frac{2}{9}$ **3.** (a) $\frac{49}{256}$ (b) $\dfrac{49}{128}$ (c) $\frac{79}{128}$

4. (a)(i) $\frac{1}{10}$ (ii) $\frac{4}{5}$ (b) $\frac{2}{5}$ **5.** (a) $0\cdot1$ (b)(i) 0 (ii) 1 **6.** (a) $\frac{9}{14}$ (b) $\frac{1}{56}$ (c) $\frac{31}{56}$

7. (a) $\frac{2}{3}$ (b) $\frac{3}{32}$ **8.** (a)(i) $\frac{7}{9}$ (ii) $\frac{47}{72}$ (b) 200 **9.** (a) $0\cdot936$ (b) $0\cdot008$

10. (a) $\frac{7}{8}$ (b) $\frac{1}{4}$

Exercise 1.2

1. (a) $k = 9$ **2.** (a) $\frac{1}{15}$ (b) $\frac{19}{30}$, $\frac{19}{22}$ **3.** (a) $a = \frac{1}{8}$, $b = \frac{5}{8}$ **4.** (a) $a = \frac{1}{6}$, $b = \frac{1}{12}$

5. $a = 1$, $b = -\frac{1}{27}$

Exercise 1.3

1. (a) 2, $1\frac{1}{3}$, 4 (b) $3\frac{1}{2}$, $2\frac{1}{4}$, $4\frac{3}{4}$ (c) $k = \frac{3}{7}$, $1\cdot36$, $1\cdot21$, $1\cdot48$ (d) $0\cdot14$, $0\cdot07$, $0\cdot23$

2. (a) $2\cdot36$, $1\cdot57$, $2\cdot74$; $2\cdot40$ (b) $0\cdot75$, $0\cdot375$, $1\cdot25$; $1\cdot55$ (c) $6\cdot33$, $5\cdot45$, $7\cdot17$; $2\cdot93$

3. $1\cdot55$, 1, $0\cdot89$, $1\cdot56$ **4.** $a = \frac{1}{2}$, $b = \frac{3}{4}$

Exercise 1.4

1. (a) $1\frac{3}{5}$, $\frac{8}{75}$ (b)(i) $3\frac{4}{5}$, $\frac{24}{25}$ (ii) 2, $2\frac{2}{3}$ (c) $\frac{8}{21}$ **2.** (a) 0, $\frac{5}{21}$ (b) 10, 105

3. (a) $\frac{1}{3}$, $\frac{1}{18}$ (b)(i) $4\frac{2}{3}$ (ii) $\frac{2}{3}$ **4.** (a) $c = \frac{3}{4}$, $a = 2$ (b) $1\frac{1}{5}$ **5.** $\frac{8}{15}$, $\frac{11}{225}$

6. $\frac{34}{25}$, $\frac{94}{625}$ **7.** (a) $\frac{1}{25}$ (b) 5, $4\frac{1}{6}$ (c) £3.96 **8.** $a = \frac{2}{5}$, $b = \frac{2}{15}$ **9.** $1\frac{1}{2}$, $\frac{11}{12}$

10. (a) $\frac{2}{3}\lambda$, $\frac{1}{18}\lambda^2$ (b) 16, £3.

Exercise 1.5

1. (a)(i) $\frac{1}{4}$ (ii) 6 (iii) $5\frac{1}{3}$ (b)(i) $\frac{1}{5}$ (ii) 3 (iii) $8\frac{1}{3}$ **2.** (a) $\frac{7}{8}$ (b) $1\frac{1}{2}$

3. 52, $595\cdot2$ **4.** (a) $13\frac{2}{3}$ (b) $\frac{3}{4}$ **5.** (a) 24 (b) $\frac{2}{3}$ **6.** $\frac{2r^2}{\pi}$

7. $0\cdot588$ **8.** $\frac{7}{10}$, $\frac{2}{3}$

Exercise 1.6a

1. $0\cdot97$ **2.** $0\cdot14$ **3.** $0\cdot98$ **4.** $0\cdot53$ **5.** $0\cdot10$ **6.** $0\cdot16$ **7.** $0\cdot03$ **8.** $0\cdot02$

9. $0\cdot32$ **10.** $2\cdot10$ **11.** $1\cdot88$ **12.** $-1\cdot93$

Exercise 1.6b

1. (a)(i) $0\cdot5$ (ii) $0\cdot951$ (iii) $0\cdot472$ (iv) $0\cdot819$ (v) $0\cdot375$ (b)(i) $4\cdot58$ (ii) $0\cdot718$

2. (a) $0\cdot758$ (b) $0\cdot829$ (c) $0\cdot094$ (d) $0\cdot381$ **3.** (a) $0\cdot5$ (b) $0\cdot012$ (c) $0\cdot344$ **4.** $0\cdot533$

5. (a) B (b) A **6.** A: ≥ 93, B: 78-92, C: 61-77, D: ≤ 60 **7.** (a) $0\cdot0455$ (b) $0\cdot3173$

8. $11\cdot88$ **9.** 25 pence **10.** (a) $0\cdot82$ (b) $12\cdot13$ cm^3 **11.** $47\cdot92$ min, $7\cdot34$ min

12. (a) B (b) B (c) A **13.** 47 **14.** (a) 2 (b) 48 (c) 239 **15.** $51\cdot28$, $20\cdot50$

16. (a) $0\cdot4012$ (b) $0\cdot0015$ **17.** £23.42 **18.** (a) $0\cdot106$ (b) 219

Exercise 1.7a

1. (a) $0\cdot162$ ($0\cdot160$) (b) $0\cdot022$ ($0\cdot021$) (c) $0\cdot935$ ($0\cdot936$)

2. (a) $0\cdot111$ ($0\cdot111$) (b) $0\cdot903$ ($0\cdot902$) (c) $0\cdot708$ ($0\cdot706$) **3.** $0\cdot973$

4. (a) 0·040 (b) 0·040 (c) 0·140   **5.** 0·864   **6.** 0·023   **7.** (a) 0·007 (b) 0·755

8. 0·250   **9.** (a) 0·016 (b) 0·849 (c) 0·016   **10.** 0·492   **11.** 0·095, 0·0004

Exercise 1.7b

1. (a) 0·104 (0·099) (b) 0·041 (0·048) (c) 0·378 (0·395)

2. (a) 0·054 (b) 0·531 (c) 0·036   **3.** 0·729   **4.** (a)(i) 0·054 (ii) 0·824 (b) 301

5. (a) 0·261 (b) 0·063   **6.** (a) 0·997 (b) 0·924   **7.** (a) 0·156 (b) 0·873 (c) 0·308

Miscellaneous Questions on Chapter 1

1. (a) 0·06 (b)219   **2.** (a) 0·75, 0·0375 (b) 1·5, 0·75

3. (i) $1\frac{2}{3}$, $\frac{2}{3}$ (ii) $\frac{2}{3}$ (iii)*0·923   **4.** 3, 3·4   **5.** (i) 0·48 (ii) 0·387

6. (ii) 2·4, (iii) 3·1875 (iv)* $1 + \sqrt{5}$, $1 + \sqrt{3}$, $1 + \sqrt{7}$.

7. (i) 0·159 (ii) 29·26   **8.** (i) b ≤ 2 (iii) a $=\frac{2}{15}$, b = 1

9. (i) $1\frac{1}{3}$ (ii) 3 (iii)* 1·29, 1·13, 1·50   **10.** 0·04   **11.** 0·6, 0·04; 3, 1

12. (i) 0·3 (ii) 4ln2 ≈ 2·773, 8; 4ln2 − 2 ≈ 0·773   **13.** (i) 0·227 (ii) 9·34

14. (b) 1·4 (c) 0·65 (d)* 1·261, 0·625, 2·064   **15.** (a) 7·9% (b) 15·5%

16. (b)(i) 0·352 (ii) 1·56 hours   **17.** (ii) $1\frac{2}{3}$ **18.** (a) $1\frac{1}{2}$ (c) $\frac{1}{8}$ (d) 2·260 (e)* 1·856

19. (b) 182-183   **20.** (a) 0·669 (b) 1·61 m   **21.** (a)(i) 8 (ii) $\frac{5}{6}$ (iii) $\frac{5}{9}$ (c)* 51 min

22. (a) 6·7%   **23.** (a)(ii) $\frac{13}{27}$ (b) 1·6   **24.** (b) 1·15, 0·0595   **25.** (b) 2·4, 0·64

Exercise 2.1

1. (a) 1 (b) 10 (c) 15 (d) 32 (e) 23   **2.** (b) 1·5   **3.** (a) 1, $\frac{1}{2}$ (b) $\frac{1}{2}$ **4.** (a) 1, 2

Exercise 2a

1. $\frac{1}{4}$ **2.** (a) 0·214 (b) 0·203   **3.** $\frac{3}{4}$ **4.** (a) $\frac{1}{8}e^{-2}$ (b) $\frac{43}{24}e^{-2}$ **5.** (a) $\frac{115}{648}$ (b) $\frac{35}{162}$

6. 4·9, 1·73

Exercise 2.2b

1. 0·0212   **2.** 0·260   **3.** (a) 0·0183 (b) 0·6288   **4.** (a) 0·7350 (b) $\frac{216}{625}$ **5.** $\frac{3}{8}$

Exercise 2.2c

1. (a) 7 (b) 41   **2.** (b) 5·92   **3.** 6, 6   **4.** 2185 cm³ **5.** $7\frac{1}{2}$, $26\frac{1}{4}$

Exercise 2.2d

1. (a) 9, 6·9, (b) 0, 38·4 (c) 1·5, 0·825   **2.** (a) 7 (b) $5\frac{5}{6}$ (c) $37\frac{11}{12}$ (d) $27\frac{5}{12}$

3. (a) 13, 13 (b) 1, 77 (c) 3, 13   **4.** 6, 6   **5.** (a) 1·9, 1·9 (b) 4·7, 13·1

Exercise 2.3

1. (a) 0·970 (b) 0·021   **2.** 0·2084   **3.** 0·1606   **4.** (a) 9, 14 (b) −1, 34 (c) 24, 1424

5. 512, 249856

Exercise 2.4a

1. (a) 0·1335 (b) 2, 25   **2.** (a) $\frac{25}{32}$ (b) $\frac{29}{32}$ **3.** 196, 18326·4   **4.** 3, $4\frac{7}{9}$

5. $\frac{3}{4}$, $\frac{27}{80}$ **6.** 15, $5\frac{2}{3}$ **7.** (a) 20, 0·5 (b) 30, 0·75   **8.** (a) 0·375 (b) 0·701 **9.** 46, 321

Exercise 2.4b

1. 0·841   **2.** (a) 0·945 (b) 0·975   **3.** 0·048   **4.** (a) 275, 1·3 (b) 0·010   **5.** 0·380

6. (a) 0·826 (b) 0·540   **7.** (a) 0·006 (b) 0·008   **8.** (a) W and Y (b) 530 (c) 0·006

9. (a) 0·100 (b) 0·261   **10.** (a) 0·052 (b) 0·029 (c) 0·794 (d) 0·239

11. (a) 0·880 (b) 0·212 (c) 0·230

Exercise 2.5

1. (a) 0·0082 (b) 0·8767   **2.** (a) 0·00135 (b) 0·07256 **3.** 0·9452 **4.** 0·8375 **5.** 44

6. (a) 0·1585 (b) 68   **7.** (a) 0·0122 (b) 24   **8.** 0·1056   **9.** (b) 0·14

10. (a) 0·07 (b) 0·04

Miscellaneous Questions on Chapter 2

1. (i) 1·4 (iii) 0·16   **2.** £430, £62.50

3. (a)(i) 0·19 (ii) 0·963 (iii) 0·039 (b)(i) 0·309 (ii) 4·464, 26·06976

4. (i) 44·65 , 2·00 (ii) 0·140 (iii) 0·313   **6.** (b)(i) 0·045 (ii) 0·871 (iii) 0·572 (iv) 0·107

7. (a)(i) 5 (ii) 4·12 (b)(i) 0·007 (ii) 0·239 (iii) 0·641   **8.** (a)(i) 0·142 (ii) 0·059 (b) 0·973

9. (b) 0·101   **10.** (a) 0·067 (b) 0·75   **12.** (a) 241·5 sec, 3·273 sec (b) 0·3228

13. (a) 0·442 (b) 0·269 (c) 0·023   **14.** (b) 0·1248 (c) 0·1401   **15.** (b) 0·6179

16. (b) 0·9301 (c) 0·0668   **17.** (b) 0·6179   **18.** (a) 0·1151 (b) 0·0548 (c) 0·966

19. (c) X and Y (d) 166, 39

Exercise 3.2.1

1. p-value = 0·0062; conclude $\mu > 10$

2. (a) p-value = 0·2076; should not reject $\mu = 2·5$

(b) p-value = 0·0114; conclude $\mu > 2·5$

3. (a) p-value = 0·1977; should not adopt (b) p-value = 0·0043; should adopt.

4. p-value = 0·006; should check machine   **5.** p-value = 0·009; conclude $\mu > 17·5$.

Exercise 3.2.2

1. p-value = 0·078; cannot support claim .   **2.** p-value = 0·52; insufficient evidence.

3. p-value = 0·118; cannot support the competitor   **4.** p-value = 0·133; not justified.

5. p-value = 0·0996; not justified   **6.** p-value = 0·115; cannot support the claim

7. (a) p-value = 0·172; cannot support Alan's claim

(b) p-value = 0·021; support claim

8. (a) p-value = 0·115; cannot reject unbiasedness

(b) p-value 0·036; coin biased in favour of head.

9. p-value = 0·089; cannot support proportion being > 55%

10. p-value = 0·123; cannot support the botanist's suspicion.

11. p-value = 0·018; support doctor's claim

12. p-value = 0·0005; the wheel is unfair

13. p-value = 0·016; conclude $\theta > 3$ **14.** p-value = 0·021; conclude $\alpha < 2$

Exercise 3.2.3

1. p-value = 0·032; conclude mean has increased

2. p-value = 0·082; too large to justify concluding that $\mu < 1\cdot4$

3. p-value = 0·067; too large to conclude that the signs are effective

4. p-value = 0·034; support the claim.

5. p-value = 0·085; too large to justify concluding that the mean has changed.

6. p-value = 0·028; conclude not of type A

7. p-value = 0·238; too large to justify concluding that the mean has increased

8. (a) p-value 0·059; too large to justify concluding that the spray is effective
   (b) p-value = 0·013; conclude spray is effective.

Exercise 3.3.1

1. p-value = 0·076; conclude that the mean is > 1243.

2. p-value = 0·044; conclude that $\mu < 9\cdot7$

3. (a) 0·055 (b) p-value = 0·092; conclude coach is beneficial

4. p-value = 0·017 > sig. level; cannot reject $\mu = 1515$

5. (a) 0·456 (b) Reject $\mu = 10$ if $\overline{X} \geq 10\cdot06$ or $\leq 9\cdot94$ (c) conclude $\mu < 10$

Exercise 3.3.2

1. 0·0861   2. 0·0355   3. (b) 0·1878 (c) accept claim if $X \geq 39$; sig.level = 0·0342

4. Conclude biased if $X \geq 31$; sig. level = 0·0595

5. p-value = 0·0355 (a) sig. level too small to justify concluding an improvement
   (b) has decreased.

6. (a) 0·0414 (b) p-value = 0·1054; sig . level too small to justify concluding that the coin is biased.

7. p-value = 0·0726; sig. level too small to justify rejecting proportion = 10%

8. p-value = 0·057; reject the claim   9. p-value = 0·058; reject the claim

10. p-value = 0·342; sig. level too small to reject the claim

11. p-value = 0·035; conclude coin is biased in favour of a head

Exercise 3.3.3

1. 0·0166; 5 ($\alpha = 0\cdot0527$)

2. p-value = 0·0749; sig level too small to conclude that the mean has decreased.

3. p-value = 0·0985 > 0·05; 9·85%

4. p-value = 0·1107; sig level too small to justify rejecting $\mu = 1$.

5. (a) 0·0148 (b) p-value = 0·0586; conclude $\mu < 2$.

6. p-value = 0·085; conclude $\mu < 1\cdot7$ 7. p-value = 0·004; conclude $\mu > 10$

8. p-value = 0·082; sig level too small to justify rejecting $\mu = 2<5$.

9. p-value = 0·0055; conclude $\mu > 1\cdot5$.

10. (a) p-value = 0·15; sig level too small to justify rejecting $\mu = 1\cdot9$
    (b) p-value = 0·04; conclude $\mu < 1\cdot9$.

Miscellaneous Questions on Chapter 3

1. 0·017; conclude $\mu > 145$ **2.** p-value = 0·02; conclude $\mu > 335$

3. p-value = 0·012; conclude $\mu > 17·6$ **4.** p-value = 0·073; cannot reject $\mu = 17·6$

5. r = 6 (sig level = 0·0101)   **6.** Sig level = 0·06; Bill's decision rule

7. 0·0985; 0·197; cannot reject $\theta = 0·09$

8. p-value = 0·068; sig level too small to justify concluding that the wheel is unfair

9. Reject $\mu = 2$ (a) if $X \geq 5$ (sig level = 0·0527) (b) if $Y \geq 8$ (sig level = 0·0511)

10. p-value = 0·138; cannot reject $\mu = 2·8$ **11.** (b) 0·166

12. (a) 0·1107 (b) 0·4497 (c)(i) K = 12 (ii) 0·260

13. (b) 26·4 (c) 0·04   **14.** (b)(i) 0·121   **15.** (a) 0·0725

17. (i) 0·0177 (ii) insufficient evidence to conclude that $\mu > 2·2$

18. (b) 0·0138 (c) 0·9216

19. (a) p-value = 0·0835; cannot support the suspicion

(b) p-value = 0·011; conclude $\mu > 2$

20. (a) p-value = 0·0531; recommend further tests;

(b) p-value = 0·0217; conclude $\mu > 1·5$

21. (b) 0·0455

22. (a) p-value = 0·1848; cannot support reduction in accident rate

(b) p-value = 0·007; conclude that the mean accident rate has been reduced

INDEX